THE DROVER'S WIFE

Leah Purcell is a multi-award-winning and self-made author, playwright, actor, director, filmmaker, producer, screenwriter and showrunner. At the heart of her work are female and First Nation themes, characters and issues. *The Drover's Wife* was first a play written by and starring Purcell, which premiered at Belvoir St Theatre in late 2016 and swept the board during the 2017 awards season, winning the New South Wales Premier's Literary Award for Playwriting and Book of the Year; the Victorian Premier's Literary Award for Drama and the Victorian Prize for Literature; the Australian Writers' Guild Award for Best Stage Work, Major Work and the David Williamson Prize for Excellence in Writing for Australian Theatre; the Helpmann Award for Best Play and Best New Australian Work; and the Sydney– UNESCO City of Film Award. The feature film adaptation of *The Drover's Wife*, written, directed and starring Leah Purcell, was released in 2021. Leah Purcell is a proud Goa, Gunggari, Wakka Wakka Murri woman from Queensland.

LEAH PURCELL

THE DROVER'S WIFE

THE LEGEND OF MOLLY JOHNSON

PENGUIN BOOKS

PENGUIN BOOKS

UK | USA | Canada | Ireland | Australia
India | New Zealand | South Africa | China

Penguin Book is part of the Penguin Random House group of companies
whose addresses can be found at global.penguinrandomhouse.com.

Penguin
Random House
Australia

First published by Viking, 2019
This edition published by Penguin Books, 2021

Copyright © Leah Purcell 2019

The moral right of the author has been asserted.

Cover image © 2020 TDW LMJ Films Pty Ltd, Create NSW and Screen Australia
Cover design by James Rendall © Penguin Random House Australia Pty Ltd
Text design by Midland Typesetters, Australia
Typeset in Adobe Caslon Pro by Midland Typesetters, Australia
Printed and bound in Australia by Griffin Press, an accredited
ISO AS/NZS 14001 Environmental Management Systems printer

A catalogue record for this
book is available from the
National Library of Australia

ISBN 978 1 76104 193 8

penguin.com.au

For Bain, with all my love

PRELUDE

1913

I love the snow gum.
Its stout trunk strong . . . beautiful coloured patterns appear when
wet; a gift from God.
The sturdy tree's limbs outstretched, waiting to take the weight of
winter . . . the weight of you.
Oh, to see these trees after an autumn shower . . . it's this rare
beauty that reminds me why I stay . . .

Late one evening Daniel Johnson sits alone on the verandah of a newly renovated homestead, reading from a tatty notebook, his lantern light low. The notebook is sixteen years old now – a collection of sketches, poems and memories. He knew he had to put it all down somehow. From the moment that spurred the four of them – Danny, Joe Junior, Henry James and little Delphi – to run into the mountains to be with them, and everything he learnt in those four short years. Their knowledge ancient beyond comprehension, and there was only so much they could share. Time and society were against them.

Now a man of thirty-two years, Danny flicks through the notebook, and the images he's sketched look as though they are animated. He stops on a page that features a full moon, the many rings he's drawn representing the moon's larger-than-normal halo of light; a powerful glow and energy, bringing unrest to the land.

Danny's thoughts race back to the moment that was the inspiration for his poem. It was suggested by her, Louisa. 'Write a poem, perhaps? A way to ease the pain ... the hurt and the loss. You don't have to show it to anyone or share it. It's just for you, Danny.'

He was taught to write poetry by Mrs Louisa Clintoff, a newspaper proprietor, a friend, a long time ago now. This poem grew from a time he remembers well, too well. The harrowing moments he has kept to himself, never shared before, not even with his siblings. It is his job to protect them, even now they're all grown.

Contained between the pages of the old notebook is the story of a great woman, strong, steadfast, reliable and loving: his ma, Molly Johnson, nee Stewart. Daughter of Jock Stewart, Scotsman and jack-of-all-trades. It's the story of a mother's love, fierce and true. And of a black man who was noble, wise and gentle, a warrior of ancient proportions – but unfortunately not Danny's father. Memories of cautious meetings, bonding and the sharing of stories. Lessons were learnt and a mutual understanding and genuine respect developed from the man to the boy and from the boy to the man – Yadaka and Daniel Johnson. There were exchanges around the fire pit, but Yadaka's stay was short. The full moon was to guide him away, north, back home to his mother's country.

But that first winter's full-moon night became momentous in more ways than one ...

ONE

1893, Late May, a few hours before midnight

I'm dead! thinks the badly beaten Molly Johnson, who lies foxing on the ground. Her bloodshot eyes dart back and forth as she gathers her thoughts. *What should I do next?* Her heavy breathing makes the loose sod under her bleeding nose and swollen lips spray.

She'd heard that when death is inevitable, life flashes before your eyes. *Well, to hell with that,* thinks Molly. *I have my children to live for.*

She knows she must bide her time. Firstly, for herself. To regain some strength and think on her next course of action, because she is no match for these two bastard stockmen. A strong cuss word crosses her mind that she would love to call them, scream to the world. But only the majestic mountain range in front of her two-room shanty will hear, and echo the word back, slapping her fair in her battered face. And there is no one here who cares for her opinion. She's just a woman.

A moon large and full with many glowing rings sits high in the night sky, silver beams spilling down to spotlight the front yard of Molly's home. Large boulders sit behind the hut and sparsely placed white sallees border the perimeter, their trunks shimmering in the moonlight, the shanty hidden in the bush to protect or hinder?

Molly cautiously lifts her head just enough to see the two stockmen as they catch their breath. The one who looks like a boy in physique wears an oilskin coat and a woman's petticoat skirt over his britches. He takes a rope from his belt. Pulled down low, his hat casts a shadow over his face. He ties up the legs of an unconscious man who lies behind the tree-trunk log that sits next to the fire pit. Ever so slightly, Molly tilts her head to see the other stockman who did all the hitting. He's helping himself to her water barrel, the barrel that she and the children fill, walking the dangerously steep decline to the banks of the Murrumbidgee, and back again. He's built like a bullock, and every bone in her body aches with pain, especially her head. But pain is not new to her. She has felt wrath before and is hardened to it. And that just may be her undoing tonight.

The older stockman with the full red beard coughs, water spluttering from his mouth. The droplets on his beard sparkle like diamonds in the moonlight.

Choke on it, ya bastard, she thinks. The distaste for him makes Molly want to spit – or is it the blood pooling in her mouth?

Fuck, she thinks, as she lowers her head. She really could be done for here. Then, there before her, she sees her axe, large, menacing and sharp. It lies in the dirt beside the old chopping block, stained on one side with something that looks like blood.

The younger stockman asks, 'How many will he make?', pointing to the unseen man.

'Thirty-eight.'

'Is that all? Slowin' up in ya old age.'

'I'm not gettin' paid.'

The older stockman pours the rest of the water over his face, and it cascades down his beard. He takes the rope from his belt and begins to knot a noose.

The night sits in silence, anticipating what's to come.

From behind them comes a gut-wrenching, 'Aaaaarrrhhh!' Molly has picked up the axe and with all her might tries to swing it with force. The stockmen spin on their heels to see her standing before them with the axe raised. She looks like a crazed woman, her hair wild and woolly like the thicket found in the high country, menacing and fierce, her stance wide. She swings the axe and the men scatter. The younger one runs, dropping the secured legs of the unconscious man heavily back onto the log.

Molly grabs at her ribs as the axe hits the ground. Sharp pain rips through her upper body – her ribs are broken. Her breath catches as she gasps with pain. She's angry that her attempt to connect with either of them has failed. *What the hell was I thinkin'?* She should have lain on the ground, pretended to have been knocked out and hoped they left with just *him*, and took their revenge out on him. Not that she would wish that upon him, but if it was to save her life and save her being taken from her children, then so be it. Sometimes that's just how things are done here, in the middle of nowhere, in the alpine country of the Snowy Mountains. *Every child needs their mother.*

Molly, feeling a fool, senses every aching part of her body: her swelling face, the red welt marks on her cheekbones, her throbbing jawline and her tender ribs. She tastes the salt of sweat and blood dribbling into her mouth as she sucks in air, exhausted, and leaning on the axe for support now. Using all her strength, she tries to lift it again. Her effort is feeble and the two stockmen laugh at her. The one with the boyish physique bares his rotten teeth, sneering. Molly struggles to hold the axe up. Her breath runs shallow and rapid.

The red-bearded stockman shifts his shotgun. 'Put it down, or I'll put a bullet through ya.'

Molly doesn't move.

'You're a fuckin' disgrace, woman.' He indicates to the pants and boots of the tied-up unconscious man; the log by the fire pit obscures his upper body. 'Puttin' ya life on the line for this low-life.' He spits the words at her in disgust.

Molly's battered face is streaked with tears, running with her sweat, snot and blood. The younger stockman asks the other, 'Ya gonna shoot 'er?'

The older stockman takes his shooting stance. Molly knows she can't win. She steps forward. He's quick to cock his shotgun; the other raises his pistol. With an anguished, guttural yell, she brings the axe down hard into the chopping block; iron to hard wood, sparks fly. She steps back, knowing her demise is near.

The red beard lunges towards her. Molly cowers. 'My children, please! My children!'

She backs away and he grabs her by the arm, his dirty, hairy fist raised, punch after punch, her head snapping back. He stops, releasing his hold. She drops. The younger stockman marches towards Molly sprawled out on the ground . . .

The tinglin' sensation starts in my feet, it is unconsciousness crawlin', coverin' me, numbin' me. My mind drifts, takin' me far away from here . . .

. . . To fields of wildflowers, and there is my cute-as-a-button five-year-old daughter. She hands me a flower crown of wild daisies that matches the daisy necklace I wear around my neck . . .

. . . The laughter of my three sons behind me, in the field of colourful wildflowers that beam so bright. They play-fight . . .

Fight. Fightin' the dark that covers my mind like a blanket . . . *Fight*, I hear. 'Fight,' I hear myself say . . .

Fight it I may, but the power in the stockman's punches is too much for me and I am gone to the darkness . . .

Before I lose consciousness I hear a ripping sound and I'm not sure if it is cloth or my flesh ...

Further out front, beyond a protruding mound of the old woodheap, the ancient snow gum stands like a sentinel, its stout trunk strong and curved like a woman's form in the moonlight, its sturdy limbs outstretched, waiting to take the weight of winter. Behind the snow gum someone watches, crouching unseen in the shadows, the full moon spotlighting the brutality before them.

TWO

One month earlier

We walk. For miles, on some Sundays. For no reason. Knowin' very
well we will not see anyone. But we do it – we walk and we talk.

Every second Sunday we put on our best, which is nothin' fancier
than what is worn for the rest of the week. Best described as rags, really.
But our faces are washed, the boys' shirts pressed, Delphi's hair set and
Joe Junior and Henry James still just fit their worn-out boots. Danny's
barefoot. He's supposed to be gettin' his da's boots this winter.

Danny is at that in-between age and stage of his growin', and the
fact that he could be off to work next year with drovin' . . . well, I shake
my head at the prospect. My little boy becomin' a man. He turned
twelve nearly two months back now. I can hold out for that day when
Danny has to go off to work, but I really don't wish it to come at all.
I need him around the house for at least another few years.

Dammit, didn't think about what that would mean. He might have
to. Things are tight. Tighter than normal with the economic depression
havin' hit us hard out this way. Sheep industry almost gone, and this
last drove, well . . . They brought fifteen thousand head down from
Queensland and Joe (my husband by status only; no love lost on him –
just for the children, really, do I do the duty of a devoted wife), he
and his usual drovin' mates meet them and take the sheep to the high
country for three months, then bring them down just before the first
snowfall in the high country, for the sale. That's been the pattern for

nearly eight years now. I don't know the men Joe works with. Not my business. I really don't care, either. It's money, support, and I get to be alone with my children, our happy time, when he's away workin', which is often.

Danny takes his mother's hand and looks at her. She's a handsome woman with all the signs of forty years of a hard life etched on her face. 'Ya right, Ma? Ya frownin' a lot there.'

I look at him, my beautiful olive-skinned boy, blond hair parted at the side – not perfectly, but he's attempted to groom himself in that 'boy' way. Handsome young man, he is. Gonna make someone a fine husband, this one.

'Just thinkin' about Alligator. Thought we might've seen him,' I say, smilin'.

Danny looks at the scrub around us, longin' for his faithful old mongrel dog to come boundin' over. 'It's only been two weeks, Ma. He'll come back.'

Alligator and Danny were inseparable when Danny was a wee one. Danny was three and Alligator a pup, full of fleas and mange. Crawled in from out behind the snow gum out front with his tail between his legs, he did. You could tell he'd been beaten. But we washed him in bush soap; wattle leaves, scrunched up, add water makes a good sud. A gin showed me this when I was a little girl. Me and Da was hidin' in the scrub. *Ssshhh, quiet now*, he whispered, putting his finger to his lips. A tribe walked through, about twenty-five yards from us. Da whistled and a gin stopped and looked around. She would have been in her mid-thirties. She dropped somethin' and then kept walkin'. About half an hour later she returned. I vaguely remember her smilin' at me, and then all I remember is her takin' me to the river and washin' me with the wattle leaves. I loved it. Foamin' suds from leaves. I thought it was magic.

We lathered the dog and then rubbed him down with goanna oil for the mange and a dab of eucalyptus at the back of his neck hopin' to keep the fleas away, and we fed him, and Danny loved him. And the dog got better. Danny named him Alligator, or that's what I thought he said. Alligator became Danny's protector – well, all our protector, really.

Danny likes to tell of the bravery of his dog, but his favourite story is the one about the time when that blasted copperhead found its way inside. If there's one thing I am scared of out here, it is the copperhead snake, the last reptile to go into hibernation, with a bite that kills. If either me or my kids get bit, we have no hope. See, that's why I trust no one with the stackin' of my woodheap. Got a blackfella to do it once, and the bastard stacked it hollow and a snake got in under. It crawled past Henry James sittin' in the dirt playin'. Not sure where Joe Junior was. He couldn't've been too far. He and Henry James are pretty much two peas in a pod; Joe Junior's only a year older.

But Danny gave chase with a stick bigger than himself. 'Get away!' I yelled, pullin' him back. The copperhead made its way inside, Alligator on its trail barkin' and bouncin' around.

That night we managed to eat outside by the fire pit, but the children got tired. Typical bush kids – as soon as the sun goes down they're off to bed, and they rise at first light. So I had to put them all up on the kitchen table, out of harm's way, to sleep. All night I sat watchin', waitin' for that bastard snake to come out. Made the night a livin' hell.

THE DROVER'S WIFE

Alligator lay at the threshold of the shanty, watchin' the shadows under the bed. Every now and then his hair would bristle and he would growl low, then nothin'.

I kept tryin' to think of a way to get the snake out. It was the beginnin' of winter, so maybe it was lookin' for its last feed? And then it hit me – food. *Of course!* I remembered an old wives' tale – the same gin some years later had told me to be careful. Through hand and body actions and with a little broken English now she warned me: 'Snakes can smell ya *thinjgun*, ya breastmilk.' I'd thought nothin' of it at the time. But with the burn of the let down of my breastmilk – Delphi was due to wake for a feed – I seized the opportunity and expressed some milk into a saucer, pushin' from the top of my breast to the nipple, milk sprayin'. I placed it as close as I could to the bed where the copperhead hid.

After about half an hour, Alligator started to growl and the hair on his back bristled. He raised himself up, ready to pounce, his growl low and menacin'. Then I saw the snake's head under the bed, and it slowly slithered over to the saucer of breastmilk. I stood, as steadily and quietly as I could, clutchin' the stick that Danny had earlier. I went to whack the snake with it but the dog got in the way. Took the blow on his nose, poor old Alligator. Tough old bastard didn't flinch. He caught that snake, shook it silly, snapped its back. Danny is so proud of his hero dog.

I stop my reminiscin', smile, and give Danny's hand a gentle lovin' pat, givin' him reassurance that my frownin' is nothin'. He scampers off again. That one is special – my angel, I call him. He's my little soulmate. This winter he's supposed to be gettin' his da's boots, but I'd love to be able to buy him a brand-new pair. He deserves it. He's seen so much. I've tried to shield him, but there's only so much I can do.

The children love our walks. We make up yarns and see who can spin the best story for the longest time. Danny is pretty good at it; so am I. Gives the children a chance to ask me questions about my life, and for some reason I open up, tell them what I know and don't know. If they were to ask me these same questions around the house, I'd close them down quick smart. Out here it's open space and open mind, maybe. I talk about things I learnt from my da and from the life we lived, and what I did as a child.

Walkin' was one of them. Lots of walkin'. Me and my da would walk almost everywhere. He worked at various jobs, a jack-of-all-trades, and we walked to where the work was. I loved it and I miss it. It kept things lively, because we'd meet people along the way, or when we managed to get a lift in a passin' wagon or a peddler's cart, we'd get to talkin', hear their stories, the short and the long of them, learnin' to decipher the lies from the truth. We'd share ours. Not a lot of detail – just what Da wanted them to know. And let me tell you, he was an expert at spinnin' yarns and keepin' 'em goin'!

'Your mother?' they'd ask quizzically, lookin' at me, and Da always replied with, 'She died in childbirth. The girl killed her.' He'd nod towards me and nothin' more would be said. And that's about all I know myself. They'd look at me with sympathy. If it was a peddler who offered us the ride, on hearin' my sad ma's story he'd often give me a trinket of some sort.

'Ma!' It's Joe Junior. He's found another wombat hole. You'd kill ya'self if ya fell in one. He's always on the lookout for me. Just as well. I'm so in my head today, thinkin' too much on the past. But that's what these walks are for, sharin' life's story.

I look to my daughter, Delphi, who is skippin' ahead, her ringlets bouncin'. I set them last night after our wash. She's naturally curly so I divide the wet ringlets where they fall, twistin' them in old bed sheets that have been ripped into strips. I also use these for medical emergencies. Her once-red skirt, now pale pink, swishes just below her knees, a big safety pin holdin' it together at the back. She has a few more years before she'll actually fit the thing. It's from one of Miss Shirley's Christian charity clothin' drives. We receive a little package yearly; it's a great help. Delphi is singin' to herself in a fine little soprano voice. 'Sings like an angel,' my da would have said. Singin' and skippin' along without a care in the world.

Without a care in the world . . . I don't think I've ever had a moment where I didn't have to care about somethin' or someone. I worried all the time when I was little, and I still worry all the time, but now I have the knowhow to make things right. I don't let my worries affect the children, although Danny is quick to pick up on them.

When I was little, I worried whether my da would die on me, especially when he was drinkin'. His drunken snores would get caught in the back of his throat and I'd nudge him awake. He'd finish off a snore and then inhale and repeat the pattern all over again: snore gets caught, I nudge, he exhales and inhales and then repeat until dawn. As the sun broke the horizon his breathin' would become even and I'd finally get some sleep. I couldn't help but think at these times, if he did die, who would take me? Who would understand me? Who would want to be bothered with me?

I worried when it rained: *Where can we shelter?* I worried when the sun was shinin': my da's pale skin would burn to a crisp. I worried when I was left alone in the shearin' shed sleepin' quarters, prayin' my da would return that night and not get into a fight that might see him arrested or dead. I worried about the next meal. I worried about where I could go to the toilet. I worried and worried. So, to see my daughter skippin' without a worry in the world means I've done my job, found my place in this world as a mother. Found my peace, I have, because of my children.

A burden buried. It'll kill me if the secret I carry down this road today is ever unearthed. Maybe that's why my head is runnin' away with me today . . .

I'm worried about more than Alligator bein' away. I'm a little worried about givin' birth, although everythin' has been goin' along all right. Nothing different to my other pregnancies that made it this far. But I'm older now, forty years old. This will be my last, I know it. Saddens me a little. There's lots to do to prepare, no money, and time runnin' out. I shake my head – Sunday walks are to rest the weary and restless mind.

I hear Delphi giggle as Danny catches her up and gives her a tickle as he passes. Of course, her other ratbag brothers' tickles are slaps and her peaceful moment turns to torment as they belt the back of her head. But she's a tough one. She might be five years old, but she stands up to her brothers. She takes off, givin' chase. The dirt flies up behind them . . .

I would run and run. Run for help. Run away when danger was near. Just run when I wasn't sure. Runnin' on my weddin' night, Joe too drunk to catch me. But the followin' night he didn't drink as much and caught me before I planned to leave. My virtue was still intact and our marriage hadn't been consummated, but this night he caught me and took a strap to my ankles. I couldn't have run if I tried. He had his way with me and it hurt, exactly as Miss Shirley said. So, I thought of the children. The babies I would have. Givin' love and bein' loved in return.

I wasn't much older than Delphi when I first went to stay with Miss Shirley, the minister's wife. Father McGuinness was older than her by ten years. She was barren but her flock was big, is what she would say. She stuck her nose into all the young mothers' business, puttin' them off from comin' to church. 'The babes are unwell,' the poor husbands would lie.

I only went to church when I was stayin' with her. 'Miss Shirley' is what we were told to call her. Her family were one of the first to settle up here in the high country – them and the Edwards, who are still in the district too. The Edwards: big family, lots of land and lots of money. Word is they have somethin' to do with the financin' of the old outpost, Cresthill, which is bein' turned into a town. That was somethin' Joe did share with me. Not sure what's happenin' with the idea of the town now, though. Haven't been into town for a while. Need to go.

Miss Shirley did look after me properly, fed me and put clothes on me that made me look like a doll. When my da went away on the droves that was the only time he left me; otherwise, wherever he went, I would go. I was a helpin' hand. Good little worker, I was.

At one time we worked for an elderly farmer, Da as a handyman and me as a feet warmer and night nurse for the elderly, near-blind farmer's wife. I would lie at the foot-end of her bed, wrappin' myself around her feet to warm them up until her husband got in. I would then move to the floor to a little bed of straw, close to the open fireplace. I had a blanket and a pillow stuffed with rags, and I was safe and warm and comfortable. I'd help her through the night, onto the commode. 'Wipe me fanny. Front to back,' she'd say. I'd pull her nightdress down and she'd lean on me as we crossed the cold floor. I never got into the bed when the old farmer was there. I was ten years old, not naive or silly. Wise beyond my years.

When I was younger, I would sneak into some of the inns my da drank at. I'd lie under the table where he sat and believe me, I saw a whole lotta things. Hands and fingers dancin' up shirts and skirts, undoin' buttons, hands divin' in like they were goin' down a rabbit hole. These lessons held me in good stead.

Today I look at my children and wonder what my da would think of them. Of me. Would he be proud of the life I've made for them?

Shieldin' them from harm? Givin' them a home to call their own and the one thing I never had – the love of a mother? I hope he's proud of me.

When I was about ten, once again stayin' with Miss Shirley and Father McGuinness, in church I would see how some of the mothers would look at their children with deep love and affection in their eyes. How they would touch them, an arm around their shoulders or a gentle hand to their cheek, to show they cared. The pamperin', the gestures of love and pride with smiles beamin' and their faces brimmin' from ear to ear. Sometimes I'd grab Miss Shirley's arm and put it around my shoulder.

I tried to see the love from my da. I guess I saw it in different ways. He'd sing to me always, when he was drunk, but it was a song sung so beautifully that he would break down and cry, and then so would I. He sang, 'Black, black, black is the colour of my true love's hair ...' His Scottish accent was thick, especially when he was drunk, but what a fine singin' voice, a voice meant to be heard. He sang many a lament, and made up a few too.

> 'There was a wee lass called Molly,
> Who always wanted a dolly.
> She said I have a name
> For when my dolly came
> And the name I shall call her is Mary!
> Singin' over and over we sing,
> Singin' over and over we will ...'

I often wonder if he was singin' about my ma when he sang about black hair, 'cause mine is a blondie-brown with a tinge of red.

My da showed me he loved me because when we were low in food and our last meal had to be the fat and pan juice from the last piece of meat from the night before, the drippin' spread over a piece of dry and sometimes mouldy bread, he would let me eat first and have the freshest piece of bread, or he would say, 'Special tonight – we'll toast that darn dry bread.' He cared because he never ever burnt the toast.

But today we walk, every second Sunday since Danny was born, and the children are content to run ahead playin' some sort of game: who can see what first, like a white brumby in a herd or a boulder that looks like a mushroom. Or guessin' what the person has seen with only the first letter as a clue. This helps with their schoolin'. Today I am left to my own thoughts. The children know the paths we take. We toss a piece of bark, rough side for the right, smooth for left, and toss it again to head off from the front or back.

I look down at my seven-and-a-half-month pregnant belly, rub a hand gently over it. Not long now. Number five, to survive, I hope. Number – *let me think, do the sums* – my tenth pregnancy. Four consecutive miscarriages, varyin' in one to two, three years apart. My last loss was at twenty-four years old and then nothin' for four years and then finally Danny arrived and survived. That's why I call him my angel. If he'd died, they would have been puttin' me in the ground beside him. I would have taken my own life. Life was too much – on many levels.

Joe Junior would ask, 'Tell us those trials and *triboolations*,' is how he would say it, 'Ma, please?' He's heard them stories many times – they all have. But that's what life stories are for: to be told and retold. To remember. The memories livin' on long after you're gone. Family history.

'He was away for eighteen months once; I think it was one of his Queensland droves. He, being my new husband Joe Johnson, ya father.'

I never call Joe Johnson their da, always 'ya father'.

I was sixteen. He was thirty-six, I think. Three months pregnant when he left. Our first drove as husband and wife. My da dyin'. Died. I buried him. The same gin helped me. Cried a river, she did. Wailed like the howlin' wind in a storm. She frightened me a little, but there was also a beauty and comfort to the sound. It's not like she knew him ... but I guess she did, thinkin' back now.

Not long after, Jack was born, their oldest brother. Joe Junior likes hearin' about him; Danny doesn't, maybe because he wants to be his ma's first and only big boy. Jack died, six months old. I rode for nineteen miles lookin' for help with my dead son in my arms. Buried him too. God, I loved him. Then my two cows died. I truly was alone then ...

My dyin' da, Jock Stewart, arranged the marriage. Da knew Joe Johnson from when he was a young fella who would drove with Jock. It was a marriage of convenience – Da was hopin' it would give me some semblance of social status and the children I so desired. He'd sat me down to tell me of his plans, he did, sober but coughin' up blood into his handkerchief. He knew I wanted children, so I could know unconditional love. I'd often spoken of not havin' brothers or sisters and he knew I didn't like being on my own.

I don't want my children to be alone. I want them to have each other should anything untoward happen to me. Oh dear me, must be my hormones. Today I'm thinkin' thoughts I haven't thought of in a long time. Is the pressure gettin' to me? Can I keep the facade up? As long as we have no visitors to the property, which is very rare anyway, or anyone askin' too many questions, I will be fine. We'll be fine. We'll play the game who can spin the biggest yarn and keep it goin' ... It's not a lie, just a game we play. Which I am good at. Learnt from the best. And then before long ... I haven't thought about the endin' yet, but somethin' will come to me when it's needed. I think good when I'm under pressure.

My Joe stands six foot five, a mountain of a man, just like the country that surrounds the shanty. He isn't ugly by any means. When we first met, I cringed at the sight of the bulge at his crotch; Miss Shirley warned me about that as well.

When I started bleedin', my da took me to stay with Miss Shirley for the week. She informed me of all things 'woman': what was required to survive a marriage, what it was to be a good wife, how I should serve him. I remember askin', 'And what does he have to do in all this? To make it nice for me?' She didn't answer.

I tried to convince my da that I didn't need a man to keep me safe. I was very capable of takin' care of myself, thanks to him and my upbringin', although I might change some things but overall, my life's journey had made me who I am. I did understand my da's position on wantin' me to marry. I didn't want to admit it, but I knew he was dyin'. So I agreed to give him peace of mind, but only on the condition that I get a proper workin' stove.

A few days later there was a proper workin' stove sittin' in the huge river-rock chimney. And it was Joe Johnson who brought it. I stood back under the old snow gum out front, peerin' around its edge, duckin' back when I thought he was lookin' over at me. He carried it into the shanty, knockin' the wall down in the process. You didn't have to do too much to knock the wall down – God only knows how it was stayin' upright. It was so flimsy, our two-room home that Da won in a card game. He was always promisin' to fix it, but he never did. He tried, but he was just too sick in the end. Joe worked on it when he was home, but it was up to me to find ways to fix things.

Once Joe had installed the stove, he lit it for me. By this time I was standin' in the shanty, partly behind the curtain that divided the two rooms. I think maybe we were flirtin', but that was the only time

I ever actually felt attracted to him. So I guess that was somethin'? What would I know, and I had no one to ask. Lookin' back now, it was hormones and nature.

I was to cook my kangaroo stew and damper, my special, and he was to stay and eat. I was taught how to hunt, kill, skin, gut, cut and cook. Da didn't make me drag it home, thank goodness, because the bloody animal was bigger than me. I knew how to do this by the time I was seven. Da made me. He said, 'If the good Lord should take me, I know ye can kill and cook ya'self a meal.'

I lived tough with Joe. He wasn't affectionate, didn't talk much, and I felt more at ease with our marriage when he was away. I tolerated 'our relations' because I knew it would bring me children.

And my da was right. Bein' married did give ya status. You were someone's: Missus Joe Johnson, my Joe, a drover's wife. Being a drover's wife gave ya a higher status to those who knew the drover's way of life. Many of the sundowners who came lookin' for work or for a slice of bread would hear ya story and move on if ya couldn't feed them, no hassle, knowin' ya was a drover's wife. But there would always be one or two rogue swagmen. They were the bastards who were sick in the head, came at sunset demandin' a bed. They'd never done a good hard day's work in their life.

Still, I preferred Joe bein' away. He drank a lot, beat me, had his way with me, left for work. That was our routine. Thank goodness he worked a lot. And thank goodness he had another sexual outlet with a willin' woman to the west. It helped ease my burden of goin' to bed with him. Usually he would satisfy himself before he went away for work and after on his way home with the willin' woman to the west. I didn't give a damn. There was one day I did, though.

*

The squabblin' of the children brings me back to reality. They're arguin' over who's won the race to the 'turnaround' point. It feels like we've only just started. My mind has raced away, all the way, robbin' me of this walk and day. I haven't even taken in the beauty of the landscape I never tire of. The tall young mountain-ash trees, straight and strong. At the base of them are the young wattle trees waitin' to bloom again in early spring, a way off now. The end of autumn isn't far away. The ghost white and silver of the tree trunks, the olive green of the shrubs beneath and the many autumn colours in the dried foliage – a rainbow of red, brown and orange litters the ground. Just beautiful. Never ceases to amaze me.

The squabblin' has escalated. 'Enough!' I hear myself say. 'Enough, now.'

Then the race is on again to see who can beat each other back to me. Delphi has started runnin' before they have finished the thought. She's a smart girl for her age. And I finally offer up some play and run towards her, my arms outstretched. She falls into me. She wins, to the boys' dismay.

Time for us to head back. There's more rain comin', it's a while off yet but it'll be here, it's the last of the autumn rains. So glad this mornin' there was sunshine. We've been indoors for days now, we needed this walk.

Is that why my head's so full of all these thoughts? Bein' closed indoors, with only walls to look at, screamin' restless children bickerin' and fightin'. Nowhere for my thoughts to escape to, just watchin' the rain washin' away my attempts to plug up the gaps in the walls. Gettin' wet, sittin' at my kitchen table, inside my home. Joe's been gone three months now. Low on supplies. Low on bullets. Not a good predicament. I'll let those thoughts go and think about them the day after next, because tomorrow is washday. If it's not rainin' ...

The life of a drover's wife. I let my thoughts dissolve on the lonely track. Hopefully they'll stay put. *Be gone*.

'Come on, you kids. With my eye I see somethin' beginnin' with B. Ba, ba, ba – B.'

'Ba, ba, ba, B for baby?' offers Delphi.

'Yes,' I say. 'Good girl. What shall we call her?'

Danny pipes up: 'Me and the boys reckon Molly if it's a girl and Matthew for a boy.' I nod, considerin'.

Delphi chimes in: 'I want Daisy for a girl and Digby for a boy.'

'Where did you get Digby from?' I ask.

'Our graveyard. The grave of the dead cat.' The boys laugh and make silly comments about the dead cat comin' to life and chasin' the baby. Digby was a wild ginger tabby cat I found. Well, it found us when we moved into the shanty. Or maybe it was already livin' there, I can't remember now. But it died not long after Da died and I buried it in the family burial plot with my da and a memory stone, a river rock for my ma.

'My turn!' yells Delphi, allowin' her voice to soar over her brothers' nonsense. 'With my little eye I see somethin' beginnin' with ta, ta, ta – T.'

'That's easy,' says Danny. 'Tree.'

THREE

The city of London never really sleeps. And on this night, Louisa Clintoff is restless.

I wake before dawn. Excited. Scared. How could anyone sleep? I turn over to see my handsome husband and gorgeous son doing exactly that, and it brings a smile to my lips. Samuel has slept between us, his cot and room all packed for the move. The Big Move, as my mama calls it. My papa calls it silly: 'Don't you know we are in the middle of a global economic depression?' And we are travelling halfway around the world to the country that is worst hit and where it all began: Australia.

An adventurer and risk-taker I am, and with the Australian Victorian government guaranteeing our safe passage and Nate desperate to find a career opportunity in something more than administration for the British Army, we have to go.

I slide as quietly as I can out of bed and go into the kitchen. Our housemaid, Clara, isn't here to nudge me awake, a warning before she opens the blinds; her work with us is finished now. She cried so much when we said our goodbyes, I'm sure the River Thames rose an inch.

Clara had been with me since I was about eight years old. That's when Mama and Papa's business and political interests really took off and had them travelling all over Britain. Clara is a dear true friend and carer. She's only eight years older than me; a big sister, is how I treated her. It was Clara who reminded me of her place, and that I had an older sister. My blood sister, Hannah, older by three years, was sent to live with my mother's older spinster sister. Aunt Bethany fussed over her when she was born: nursed her, bathed her, took her for long walks in the park. People honestly thought Hannah belonged to my aunt.

When Hannah was five, Mama could see the strong bond between them – so much so that she decided to send Hannah back with Aunt Bethany for a little holiday. The holiday was constantly extended. In her letters to Mama, Aunt Bethany spoke about what a great help and treasured companion Hannah was. I think back now and perhaps we should have asked Hannah what she wanted or what she thought about her situation. She did come back for holidays but she was distant from us, whether out of resentment or because she had succumbed to our aunt's reclusive ways. Mama always said that Hannah was a lot like her older sister Bethany, long before she went to live with her.

It was those hermit habits that also led to Hannah's early death. I can't help but blame myself for not trying a little harder, as we got older, to bond with her. To let her know that she could share things with me as sisters should. Or connect with her so I could see the signs that she was not safe in her marriage. Mama said we can't change what happened to Hannah, but we can make damn sure it doesn't happen to others. Hence our work for the women's movement, for battered wives.

The whistle of the kettle makes me jump. It's so loud that its echo bounces around the bare room. Swiftly I lift it from the flame and pour steaming-hot water into my little green teapot. Three twirls to the right then three twirls to the left, a trick for a quick strong brew, then I pour the hot black liquid into my favourite teacup. I only ever use one cup for my tea. A squeeze of lemon and then I walk out to enjoy, for the last time, my garden. My small courtyard garden is my favourite place. I'm not a gardener in the true sense of the word but I do appreciate the beauty and scent of a flowering plant or tree. Planting the garden was Lisbeth's idea. She is my very best friend. We were born seven days apart. Our mothers were acquaintances, but it wasn't until four years after our births that we met at a park and got playing and our mothers got talking, and we have been best friends ever since. Lisbeth and I told people we were twins, seven days apart. Lisbeth is much more girly and romantic while I am the tomboy and the realist. We balance each other.

My garden is a mismatch of self-sustaining plants, the kind that just need the odd watering and pruning, like the climbing rose bush I have in one corner. Finally it's worked its way up to cling to some wire Nate placed on the side wall.

I can't help myself – I must sit down there amongst my plants, since it will be the last time for a long time. I sit on the bottom step. There are lavender bushes to my left and right, and daisies that I planted in memory of my grandmother, whose name was Daisy Margaret. She was the topic of my first published poem.

Daisy Margaret
A young lady of grace and beauty,
A mother of pride and joy,
A grandmother of care and comfort,
A great-grandmother sick and dying.

A young lady of health and beauty,
A mother who didn't indulge pleasantries, no ill will or lie,
A grandmother to set examples,
A great-grandmother sick, in pain and dying.

A young lady I did not know,
A mother of activity I did not see,
A grandmother as I know her,
A great-grandmother I see, sick, in pain and dying.

Papa thought the poem was morbid but Mama could see my maturity and potential. She rewarded me for my efforts and ran it in their newspaper. I was ten years old and very dramatic.

My parents, Dawn and Reginald Lorens, are publishing proprietors, both writers for the publication they print, both progressive left-wing revolutionaries who are solely responsible for my views. The apple did not fall far from the family tree, believe me. Their strong focus on women's issues features heavily in their work. It was a focus for them before Hannah's death, but her passing drove them to greater involvement. I can't help but think they too felt a little responsible.

My feistiness comes from Mama, my drive from Papa – well, them both, really, but it was Papa's persistence that got their business up and running. And my social conscience is from them both. I have always been enthusiastically interested in my parents' work. At first it was the physical labour of printing the paper that had me wishing to follow in their footsteps: I respected them both deeply for the hours they put in then, and still do to this day. The technology of the late 1880s and early 1890s has made things easier for them, but Papa is getting on. He's not a young man anymore.

Mama has always been an active participant in the women's movement in Britain. She writes about women's education, women's economics and legal rights, battered women and the temperance movement. After losing Hannah at the hands of her husband, and enraged at the silence around such a dangerous epidemic, we took it upon ourselves to publicly shed light on the subject. I hope to bring the same awareness to the women in the high country of Australia. My plan is to give them a voice through my own publication, a monthly women's journal that will focus on the gamut of issues that affect a woman's life: from hard-hitting interrogations of education, childbirth, economics and battered wife's syndrome to the more genteel subjects of poetry, knitting and cooking. I will call it *The Dawn*, after Mama, that name also being my sister's middle name. Hence my added excitement for our Australian adventure: setting up my own business and actively engaging with the local communities of the region. I have clear and precise goals. So much so that I am taking one of Papa's old mimeographs, plenty of wax paper and bottles of ink.

In the corner of my eye, I see the orange of my various chrysanthemums. I turn to them, thinking the sun has broken out from behind the cityscape and the smog. The assortment of colours was amazing when they first came to bloom. It was as if a rainbow had landed in our garden! What joy they brought. Just what Nate needed in his life: colour.

When we were first courting, we would sit for hours on Saturday mornings in the garden before my plantings, drinking tea, nibbling on fruit and talking, as we got to know each other. I respected Nate so much when he finally spoke to me about his 'dark place'. I remember asking him what it was like. He took a moment to find his words, then said it was like walking with each step weighted behind your larger-than-life shadow, and when you try to get ahead, you trip over your own feet and land heavily, always face first. There's a constant compression in your chest, shallow breaths, heart racing like it's jumping out of your body.

I couldn't imagine Nate ever having to deal with this. To look at him, other than his limp on bad days you just would not expect him to have this torment. I have only ever witnessed its grasp on him once, and it broke my heart. But we clung to one another and promised that patience and love and time would get us through. And it has. I have asters in my garden because of something I read: that in ancient times the burning of their leaves would ward off evil spirits. I thought they might help Nate and his dark clouds of doom.

The aster is supposedly a talisman of love and patience, and patience is what we both know is required for our marriage to last. Love we have in buckets, but patience for each other's little bouts of acrimony – because we can both be strong-headed fools at times – is greatly needed. We have been together for five years now and have learnt very quickly when that patience is needed. At those times I go into the garden and pick that very flower to place around the house. The asters are blue, like Nate's eyes, and their scent is light and breezy, like his nature on a good day, which is most days. The flower I planted for myself is the white columbine. It feels like it belongs in a fairy garden with its little bell-shaped flower when it is closed and layers of elegant petals when it opens. Delicate and divine femininity is what I see in this flower. Not quite how I would describe myself, but I planted it as balance for me. And what else? Oh yes, geraniums. I have two colours, a pink and a red, which I adore.

I remember a night when we sat out here in the garden, taking in its heavenly scent. By this stage we were a year into our courtship and our marriage was only weeks away. It was the garden's first bloom, and planned for our wedding. I'd had a little wine to drink at lunch with a few of my friends and Lisbeth teased me about the magic that lives in my little garden. 'Beware of the full moon tonight. Be very careful, Lou Lou,' she said, giggling behind her handkerchief, her eyes dancing with mischief.

Nate had chosen to give up drinking, which was a blessing for his melancholia, so on this night he thought I was quite the act. But he was very patient; see, I was very tempted to give over to my great urge to feel his manhood inside me. I get this talk and these thoughts from

Lisbeth, you know. Well, I can't really blame her – let's say she liberates my thinking. But ever the gentleman, Nate sent me home. Even though the thought of intimacy drove him insane. A splash with cold water was what changed his mind and mood. As for me, a spoonful of a concoction my mother had made up that cured everything and stripped paint off walls, a bucket and a cool wet washcloth and the room beginning to swirl changed my mind of any thought of tomfoolery.

We did become intimate before our wedding night, though. You couldn't blame me. Nate is a strikingly handsome, broad-shouldered man with muscles rippling in every part of his body, one of those men who are just naturally well built and retain muscle even if they haven't done a bit of physical exertion. He has piercing blue eyes that penetrate your very soul. And a way of looking at you: those brilliant baby blues turn into azure puddles of innocence, like a little puppy.

I instantly said yes when he asked for my hand in marriage. I thought I owed it to him and myself, considering I had him chase me for six months saying no to every invitation he offered: to functions, dinners, breakfasts, lunches and walks in the park. He would come to our business and take out ads for the military. My father refused him the advertising space at first, but then the money was too good to pass up; I'm sure Nate put his own wage into the offer. And his argument was that my father must allow the military to have their say as they had allowed him to have his. It was only a recruiting ad, and my father understood the need to defend one's country. He is against us going out and being the aggressors of war and against the gains the country makes from war, like the South African Boer War, for example, the gold and diamonds. But when Nate came to take out his final ad, he said it was final because if I did not start courting him, he would burn his house down and move to the country. This time he made sure I couldn't say no. If I didn't accept his invitation to a picnic, besides burning his house down he would place an ad in my parents' paper stating all the times I had said no to him.

It was more for the safekeeping of the house than the embarrassment of the ad that I said yes. Lisbeth and I had followed him one Sunday afternoon to see where he lived, and I fell in love with the modest Victorian two-storey house. It wasn't too large or arrogant in its appearance; it was homely and something about it appealed to me. And Lisbeth said if I didn't say yes she would ask him to court her. So I said yes and have not regretted it for one second.

All these precious memories coming back to me. Key moments in our journey together. And now, as scary as it is, we are about to embark on our next chapter in another country, at the height of a global economic depression. Maybe Papa's right, we really are silly.

The morning sun will soon be rising over dirty, dusty London. We live in the Royal Borough of Greenwich on the very edge of the boundary just before the big bend in the River Thames where the Isle of Dogs protrudes on the opposite side. Nate inherited the house. His brothers opted for the countryside with their wives and children. On Nate's father's retirement from the British Army his parents also headed to the countryside, closer to the grandchildren. This was long before I joined the family and our son Samuel Adrian Clintoff was born. Nate's parents are still very active in the army, mainly attending functions and charity events, and often reside with us when they are in town.

I do love London and I will miss her greatly. Especially my garden and my star jasmine, evergreen, its ovate leaves claiming my back wall that borders a back lane, the vine's density covering the mouldering sandstone and its sweet, soft-scented little white flowers so pleasant in the spring and summer months.

When I first moved into the house, it was very much a bachelor's pad. Nate only used half of it. Sparse furnishings. Curtains always closed. When we first met, he was in a dark place as he calls it. It was after our wedding – well actually, through our courting – that I slowly turned his house into our home, shedding a bit of light and softness on his darkness. But I was aware that it was his home and I didn't want him to feel out of place, so the parlour is decorated more for him than myself. I do have a touch of femininity around the bay window that overlooks our back garden. I do try to show my womanly side.

It was Lisbeth's suggestion that I put the star jasmine in to cover the mouldering sandstone back wall. She is such a romantic, suggesting that at night when the vine was in flower we could sit out there and be swept up in its heavenly scent. And we did and still do. When there is a light breeze blowing, the scent wafts through the parlour to the main dining room and the sitting room, a welcome relief from the pollution of London and the smell of sewage from the river. I will miss pruning the star jasmine, my meditation – especially when I have writer's block, or I need to think something through. Nate stands watching from the back verandah, then a deep masculine chuckle escapes him, bringing my attention back to reality, to him. His smile can unblock anything. He always says, 'You'll cut right through that wall one day.'

The first time I exhaled on seeing him was not out of love or admiration: it was out of frustration! I had attended the rally against the South African War; many opposed the British presence there. Papa was speaking at the protest. He had been very vocal in his newspaper articles, but he used a pseudonym so as not to be arrested. But today at this rally he was going public. The military sent a clerk as a representative who would also have the opportunity to respond. I was appalled on seeing Sergeant Nathanael Clintoff. He looked like he'd had a rather late night with his shabby appearance, and he reeked of alcohol. He fell asleep part way through my papa's speech but blast it, I couldn't take my eyes off him. *A lost soul*, I thought, as I watched him limping around the grounds when he had the energy or ambition to get up and hand out the army's pamphlets that outlined their position on war. But my pity was short-lived as I found out he was from an affluent military family and should know better and have more respect for himself, his family, his purpose and job.

Feeling warmth on her toes, Louisa is roused from her thoughts: the sun's first ray has finally spilt across the garden. She hears the pitter-patter of little bare feet and the hushed, dulcet tones of her husband talking gently and encouragingly to their son. On seeing his mother sitting in the morning light, the boy runs to her open arms and she sweeps him up, devouring his chubby cheeks with kisses. Nate stands back marvelling at this beautiful sight. *What a vision to wake up to*, he thinks, as he leans in to kiss her good morning. His stomach churns with hunger and excitement for the journey they are about to embark on. 'I'll prepare us something to eat.'

It was Louisa who had persuaded Nate to take up the offer to travel to a faraway land. It was like a fairytale. What an adventure! She could see his soul dying even though he had worked tirelessly on his 'dark place' – 'melancholia' was his mother's preferred word. It came from the injury he'd received in the South African War, shrapnel ripping through the thigh of his left leg and rendering him unfit for action. Reassigned to clerical duties, which he hated, he'd been chained to a desk for eight years by the time Louisa marched into his life. He gives thanks for that every day. She was his ray of hope, his reason to live and crawl back from his darkness, which at times rendered him disabled. There were days when he could not get out of bed but that has not happened since they married, five years ago now.

In the first two years of their marriage Louisa organised adventurous trips to the countryside. And during this time Nate worked his way to sergeant status. It was her encouragement that led him to take up the offer of moving to Australia; the new upholder of Her Majesty's law for the newly formed town that had been a troopers' outpost in the Snowy Mountains of the alpine country.

'Why not?' Louisa had squealed with excitement when he first broke the news of the offer. 'Think of the adventure! Think of the control you can have. Not sitting at a desk, filing paper after paper. A man of the town, your town, bringing law and order, building something from the ground up. Nate, how wonderful!'

Nate could only smile and admire his intelligent, beautiful wife. He knew she was right and this trip would be perfect for his soul and sense of pride. As he justified his own thoughts, Louisa was talking at a hundred miles an hour, flitting around the room, her arms waving, with a light skip to her step. God, he loved her.

He always cringed when he thought back to their first meeting, at a rally where her father had spoken.

I was still drunk from the night before, and probably smelt like the whores I had bedded. Anger, hate and self-pity had raged through me since my return from South Africa, and the only way I knew to deal with it was to drown it with alcohol and mind-numbing romps in filthy sheets of sin and bed mites. I'd been existing under a dark cloud for years, consumed by self-loathing. On a few occasions I did need urgent medical attention; miraculously I was revived, and I walked straight back out to the closest inn.

I felt her looking at me, but I didn't care. I was used to people staring and tut-tutting their disapproval. But when I did catch her eye for just a fleeting moment, there was something in it that sent a charge through my body. I sat bolt upright as if struck by lightning, but she was gone, lost in the crowd. It was only later that I saw her again, standing alongside her father after his rousing speech against war.

Then I knew it would never work. I come from a strong military family. Me, my father and my older brother – we all fought side-by-side in the Transvaal Rebellion, each of us receiving medals of bravery. The Boer War was our father's last hurrah, and after my injury Mother swore there would be no more fighting for anyone, prompting my two brothers to take to the land. Father could still get his kicks, as Mother put it, and remain close to the military by attending military functions. So, my mother dearest was more than happy that my new position in the military was to sit behind a desk.

It wasn't until everyone had left the rally and I was cleaning up my station, and she her parents', that we bumped into each other. With our heads, to be precise. We both bent to pick up pamphlets from the ground. She called me a big buffoon and all I did was laugh, which of course was the wrong thing to do. But I finally managed to say that I agreed with her and if she would do me the honour of joining me for dinner, I would sincerely apologise for my buffoonery and make up for the lump that was swelling upon her pretty forehead. She blushed a stunning powdered pink, tightened her lips to a pout, slammed her hand to her forehead and marched off. I was instantly in love. For the first time in eight years, there was a lightness in my soul.

The bacon fat spits, hitting Nate's bare chest and bringing him out of his thoughts. Piling three plates with fried eggs, bacon and the last of the bread, he joins his little family on the back steps in Greenwich for the final time. Louisa keeps Samuel occupied with stories of what a grand adventure they will have on the high seas to a land down under called Australia.

It was when Louisa and Nate were checking the world globe in the sitting room that they came up with the phrase 'down under'. Louisa had put herself in a rather awkward position to see, her hair cascading to the floor, blood running to her cheeks. She had tipped herself upside down to read the globe as to where exactly Melbourne was, saying, 'It's kind of down and under, isn't it?', her nose twitching with curiosity. She stood up too quickly and fell into Nate's arms, and they laughed. 'We might fall off if we are not careful,' she had proclaimed.

And this morning we are about to set off on that very trip, down and under, and I pray we won't fall off. Or that I won't fall back into my depths of darkness. *My fear is normal. It's all right to be afraid. It's all right to have high expectations of what I am required to do. And it's all right to not reach them, as long as I have goals and try.* This is my mantra to help keep my clouds of doom at bay. Louisa came up with them. I'm not sure they work but what I do know is that at the end of her proclamation was her smile — and that is what I think really works. But this morning I will keep my thoughts of despair to myself.

Breakfast complete, their bathing and personal hygiene attended to, there is a knock at the door. The footmen have arrived to load the last of their trunks and the three of them into the horse-drawn carriage and take them on their final journey through the city streets of London to Portsmouth, about sixty miles away, for their departure.

Louisa sits forward, perched at the window like an excited child.

I don't know whether it is from sheer delight and excitement at our voyage that lies ahead, but the city of London is filled with an energy I haven't felt before. The buildings aren't so daunting and dark, the low clouds not so heavy and dreary. People walk with a skip in their step and some even turn to smile at us as we go, moving down the cobblestone streets.

Samuel is on Nate's lap looking out the other window, waving at people as we pass. Every now and then he cheers and giggles at whatever Nate is whispering in his ear. Nate bounces him on his good knee and every time there is a bigger-than-normal bump in the road, Samuel is bounced into the air. Oh, what joy to hear my son and husband laughing and cheering.

Our carriage comes to an abrupt halt. Both Nate and I stretch our necks to see why. We have time on our side, so it isn't too much of a worry. Nate places Samuel in my lap and leans out the window to speak to the footman at the back, who is positioned slightly higher. I can't quite make out what is being said.

Nate sits back down and informs me as he takes Samuel that there has been an accident ahead. A cart has overturned, there is someone hurt and produce all over the street. We could wait until it is cleared or we could take another route – not one favoured by the rich or those with precious family possessions; if you go there, particularly at night, you will surely be robbed. But since it is eight-thirty in the morning, surely the riffraff are sound asleep? We choose the alternative route, not wanting to risk waiting until the clean-up is done just in case it takes longer than expected.

We are to depart on the SS *Aberdeen*, 'a triple expansion steam engine single screw' is what Nate told me. Having no idea what that meant, I nodded enthusiastically as he briefed me on our seaworthy carrier's details. She travels at 12 knots, capacity is 695 passengers and the ship – 'she' as he fondly calls her, as if 'she' were an acquaintance of ours – was just refurbished last year, 1892. And 'she', the SS *Aberdeen*, will be departing promptly, whether we are there or not. To sit and watch a clean-up would therefore drive me insane this morning, so we opt for the back roads and laneways as the better option for our sanity and adrenaline.

As we start off again, I decide to check the map of the route we will take to get to Australia. I need to find some focus. We are to head down the west coast of Africa, around the Cape of Good Hope and then east to the Australian west coast, then head further down and under the country. Knowing the world is round, I still can't help imagining us falling off its edge. The voyage will take approximately eight weeks with favourable winds. We will be travelling first class courtesy of the British Army and the Victorian and New South Wales governments. Our voyage is a direct sail to Melbourne. We have been warned that we will encounter some rough and dangerous waters, especially in the Bass Strait, the last leg of the home stretch. It thrills me but also puts the fear of God through me.

Once again our carriage is stopped abruptly, but this time by the low gruff voices of men in the lane outside, which make this stop far more worrisome than the first. I have a feeling that this encounter will not end well. Nate quickly swings Samuel to me, at the same time drawing the blinds. He delivers a quick, curt instruction to get down and stay down, and then he is gone.

There is an inaudible exchange of words and then I hear the scuffle of feet and a commotion. Thumps and bumps at the side of the carriage. Heavy grunts of exertion. But as instructed I stay down and stay put. Besides, I have Samuel to think of.

Dammit. The bastard caught me on the blind side. The footmen have squared up to the other two men who came at them from the sides, out of the darkened doorways of the laneway. I'd hoped these thieving lowlifes would be sleeping. They demand our trunks and today I'm just not having it. And a good fight to settle the nerves feels right. I can see they have no weapons and are not your robust burly type – they're wiry and young, and would normally be the lures or lookouts. Maybe they thought they could impress their lot with a morning haul.

Bastard! Another hit to my ribs. I come back with a left-right and body-blow combination. This bastard can fight and is going toe-to-toe with me. Time for something drastic: this is taking up our travel time. I pull my pistol and they back off quick smart. One of the footmen has been knocked out but is slowly coming to. They drag off one of their own who hasn't fared so well either. We help our man up and onto the back of the carriage and move off, taking the first right turn we can to get us out of the laneway for fear they may go and get help. Or, worse still, weapons.

What a bloody fool I am. I didn't consider hard enough the safety of my wife and son. What if . . . I can't even bring myself to think it. We make haste and are now back on the main road to Portsmouth for our departure. I do feel better for the fight, though.

'I did try to talk them out of robbing us,' are the first words I say to Louisa as I scamper back into the carriage.

Once she has finished looking me over for injuries, she scolds me, and fair enough. Samuel, the little devil, has a smirk on his face; he knows very well what has happened.

We arrive in Portsmouth and I help unload, my ribs a little sore. We board the SS *Aberdeen*, all very excited as we explore our room and the ship's decks. Then we set sail, pushing back from the docks, waving to others' loved ones, Samuel squealing with delight at the excitement around him. My parents wanted to see us off, but we told them we didn't want to make a fuss, and to keep things calm for Samuel's sake. Not to mention my anxiety. No goodbyes. And we are away.

Everton. Snowy Mountains. Alpine country. The high country, New South Wales. Australia. I hope I can achieve what is required. The new keeper of the peace of the newly formed town. It was once an outpost, Cresthill. There to uphold the law and implement legislation. A town. My town. Makes me feel good about myself, best I have felt in a long time.

FOUR

Our voyage to Australia was uneventful, which is probably a good thing. My right arm got a workout, though. Not through my writing, as one might think. If I wasn't patting Samuel to sleep I was rubbing Nate's back, soothing him while he heaved into a bucket. Bless him. Nate suffered seasickness for almost the entire journey, but swore it was something he ate. It did eventually subside.

Sailing the Southern Ocean along the coastline of this great southern land was the most beautiful thing I saw the entire trip. I was thrilled to think what the rest of this country had to offer. They were right about the waters of the Bass Strait, but we got through and we made it to Melbourne, Australia. To the land down under, alive. And Mama, happy to report we didn't fall off!'

Louisa writes to her mother from a room at a guesthouse in Melbourne. They're stopping here for a week before they set off on the next leg of their journey to the New South Wales highlands. She takes a moment to think about the tasks at hand. Lots to be done: provisions bought, collected and sorted; travel route planned and studied; briefings for Nate – many briefings for Nate – and trunks and cases checked. Louisa looks out the window overlooking a park, the lace curtain moving gently in the light breeze.

I do like the city of Melbourne, Mama, lots of parks, very green with tall eucalyptus trees – gum trees, as they are fondly called. Beautiful, tall trees with white and silver trunks and long, slender olive-green leaves, rather calming to look at. And something I believe is truly iconic to Australia. The trees smell amazing and are used for medicinal purposes as well. But dangerous: their other nickname is the 'Widow Maker'. Apparently, many a drover's wife has been made a widow before her time, their drover husbands taking respite under such a tree to then have a branch fall and kill them dead in their slumber. I must remember that and warn Nate. I was worried about snakes and spiders, but now a tree! Oh dear!*

The air is fresh here, Mama, and I can see Nate's soul relishing it already. He feels so alive here; seeing him happily organising and being so involved is a delight. His leg is holding up well because he's been doing his physical therapy. He's got a new lease on life. And Samuel has pink in his cheeks and runs for hours when we manage to get him to a park. He takes off his shoes and just goes! The other women I have met are friendly enough and very considerate of us, but they are of the higher class. There is more wealth here than I had imagined, considering the global economic situation now. And the Australians are very loyal to the monarchy – dare I say it, frightfully more so than us. The majority of the women I have met are not as interested in the politics of the country as I would have thought or hoped, nor really stand for anything of substance. I say this with some confusion because it is Australia leading the charge in the women's suffrage movement. But then again that is coming from the city of Adelaide, which I hope to visit at some stage. Maybe only the few I have met seem this way. And perhaps it is my arrogance towards the higher society. So, I will not judge as I have been brought up not to, but I will keep in touch with a few, and

*encourage their interest in the governing of their country's ideals –
to advance and give voice to equal rights and equality for all women
here. I do feel I can persuade them though, in the future perhaps?
Particularly as they are women of influence, who have come from
or have married into money. I wonder if they would financially
support my monthly women's journal idea, Mama? Perhaps that
could be a way in for them? Or is this my ego talking, Mama? One
must laugh at oneself, oh dear me!*

Louisa pauses from her letter-writing to contemplate this. *The
future. My future here in Australia. Australia. I would never have dreamt
in a million years that I would be destined for Australia.* She's roused
from her thoughts by Samuel, who has woken from his nap. *Time for
something to eat and a walk in the park.* Nate should be back soon as
he promised he would join them. Hopefully bringing the trunk she
requested.

There is a ball tonight in honour of the Right Honourable John
Adrian Louis Hope, the Earl of Hopetoun and Governor of Victoria,
and the Honourable George Turner MP. Prior to the ball there is a
private dinner in the Clintoffs' honour.

Louisa rifles through a trunk looking for a dress she often wears
to occasions like this. Not that there have been many. Not her or
Nate's thing really, balls or fancy functions. But she is glad she packed
it. She wasn't going to, but being the wife of the new law and order of
Everton, she thought an evening gown might come in handy. *What
a privilege*, Louisa gushes to herself, *an evening of fine dining and
dancing*. She's hoping Nate has grabbed the right trunk from storage.
At last, a final heave as she retrieves her dress from the very bottom.
A beautiful red-and-white full-length ball gown made of a satin-cotton
blend with lace trim spills from the trunk, cascading to the floor.

It has three-quarter-length poet sleeves with a bow detail on the cuffs. The red satin stomacher matches the dress skirt of the gown, white satin with detailed fine red embroidery on it. The paleness of Louisa's skin, her dark auburn hair and brown, almond-shaped eyes that change colour with her moods enhance and complement her dress beautifully. When she is concentrating or angry her eyes turn to deep, dark pools of chocolate, and when she is excited or staring lovingly at her husband and son in a moment of sheer bliss, they turn to a burnt toffee speckled with gold, especially when sunlight hits her face at a certain angle.

Nate loves the magic in her eyes and adores her in this dress. He gave it to her for a birthday. Louisa doesn't much care for the bows on the sleeves, but she knows how fond Nate is of this gown, and his reaction when she first tried it on was so priceless that she dared not say a word about her dislike of the bows. And on special occasions she does like to dress up and be the lady her husband needs by his side.

Oh dear, she thinks. *Who will help me dress?*

As if by some mysterious power from the other side of the city, the wife of Governor Hopetoun has read her very thoughts. 'Lady Hersey Alice Eveleigh de-Moleyns, daughter of the 4th Baron Ventry,' the footman announces on presentation of the dresser she has sent for Louisa's convenience. Louisa is very flattered and thankful for the kind gesture. Later she finds out from the whispers of the gossiping wives of lower-ranked politicians that Lady Hopetoun is known for her haughty manner.

The ball is extravagant and quite unnecessary considering Australia has just emerged from its economic depression, and especially with the ministerial instability in the Melbourne office. But Louisa does need to look the part – and besides, the Clintoffs are the special guests. But the ball is not just for them: their arrival coincides with the announcement of the Honourable George Turner running in the election for premier of Victoria the following year. He and the governor are both passionate about the push for Federation.

Louisa exhales. Riding in a carriage through Melbourne is a delight – the early evening fresh, a crispness to the air, her handsome husband by her side. *He's done a fine job in the selection of his attire this evening,* she thinks, *hiring his suit himself.* He looks dashing and proud, and Louisa can barely take her eyes off him. Oh, how she loves him.

Later, as talk swirls around the room like the hemlines of the dancing women's gowns, Governor Hopetoun flamboyantly holds court, boasting of the success of his extravagant evening. Neither Louisa nor Nate could have predicted that it will be another seven years of hardship before their adopted country gets back on its feet. Perhaps if the ball's outlandish budget were redirected into the economy, prosperity may have arrived a little sooner.

Finally, we arrive at our destination and footmen are run off their, well, feet. The carriages have all converged at once, following strict instructions for the presentation of the arriving parties – it's chaotic but seems to be working to plan. While we wait, I take in my surrounds.

The Melbourne Town Hall is a large, stately building with a central body and a wing either side. The clock tower stands to the very right of the building, not central as most are. Inside, the ballroom is very grand indeed, elaborate chandeliers hanging from the soaring ceilings. I was not aware of the high society Melbourne harbours.

A string quartet plays as we make our entrance. We are ushered straight to Governor and Lady Hopetoun. I thank her for her assistance, telling her it was as if she read my mind. We share pleasantries, but it's her husband who most intrigues me. He is wearing hair-powder, even though he is not wearing a wig. With his hair receding, particularly at the sides, the powder gives his natural hair the dignified and polished look of old – living up to his forefathers' dress style, I suppose, which is no longer considered fashionable, but he is the Right Honourable John Adrian Louis Hope, the Earl of Hopetoun GCMG and Governor of Victoria. He seems to have a young, mischievous spirit and I like him. He says if we were staying longer he would love to take us on one of his informal horseback tours. He and Nate of course speak about war, but the governor's poor health prevented him from joining the army and seeing any action. He was educated at Eton, where he rowed and was on the debating team. He then went on to the Royal Military College, Sandhurst, passing in 1879. He and Nate compare dates, finding that had Governor Hopetoun been in better health, Nate would more than likely have fought under his command in South Africa. Governor Hopetoun ushers Nate away to a less crowded area for further chat.

We have arrived to interesting times in Australia. There is a push for the six separate British self-governing colonies to unite and form the Commonwealth of Australia, keeping their own form of governance but agreeing to a federal government that would be responsible for matters affecting the whole nation. I remember Papa mentioning this in a conversation with Nate's father at our final family dinner together; considering the two men have totally different views on war, they get along quite well. Samuel was feeling unwell and took my attention away from their conversation. I did enjoy listening to my papa's worldly knowledge and will miss our talks dearly.

Finding myself alone, I take in the particulars of the room: ladies in lavish ballgowns, the fine material of the draped curtains, the polished wooden wall panels and the design on the wallpaper. As I turn to take another drink, I meet Mrs Rosa Morgan Turner; our hands reach for the same glass. She observes, 'There is only so long you can stand staring at and admiring wallpaper.'

We laugh, introduce ourselves and then proceed to investigate each other, our husbands and our mutual interest in women's rights. I discover Rosa is the wife of the man for whom this ball is also in honour, and that we are the special guests for the dinner prior. She is a woman after my own heart. She can see that this isn't quite my norm. The extravagance makes me a little uncomfortable, as it does her. Her husband loathes this type of unnecessary spending. 'The money that went into this night would have contributed greatly to the advancement of women and the women's rights movement my mama fights so hard for in Britain, and most certainly in Australia,' I tell her.

To my delight Rosa agrees. She informs me of the advancement of the movement in South Australia, where women have the right to vote. I eagerly inform her of my own knowledge on the subject. She is travelling there soon, to Adelaide, for a function to help raise funds for the movement. She asks where I might be in the coming months, and to my misfortune, I tell her, 'Settling into the lifestyle of Everton, somewhere in the Snowy Mountains of the alpine country.' She informs me of her husband's standing, and hopes that once he is elected he will bring light to the issue of equality for women and give them the vote in Victoria. Oh, how this talk excites me!

Although Mr Turner is considered frugal, prudent, unyielding and self-sacrificing in his wife's opinion, it is his policy of strict economy and balanced budgets, raising taxes and cutting spending that is restoring confidence in the Victorian people. Everyone is hurting, and they desperately need to hear from someone who has a common-sense and practical approach. Will this do anything to relieve the effects of the depression, though? This is yet to be seen. She goes on to tell me that Mr Turner is part of the Australian Natives Association. I am thrilled to hear that he is for the advancement of the Aboriginal people, as I understand they have not been favoured or considered in the colonisation of this country. There is an uneasiness when this topic comes into conversations and it is always quickly deflected. But to my horror, I learn that the Australian Natives Association is for white men only, and the term 'natives' means the first generation of Australian-born white men! I have a great interest in learning more about the Aborigines' customs and plight, but I won't be talking to the Honourable George Turner on the subject.

We assure each other we will write and when the time comes I will be delighted to accompany Rosa to Adelaide, or work with her on forwarding the women's movement in the south. She also speaks of a small country just off the east coast of Australia called New Zealand and their progress on the plight of women. I question my forwardness but think *Why stop now?* so I bravely ask Rosa if she will consider writing a page on the function in Adelaide for my monthly women's journal. I tell her of my plans and she does not hesitate in her reply: 'I would be honoured and thrilled to.'

I follow Rosa into the dining room, where we are placed at opposite ends of the very long and elegantly arranged table. We bid our farewells and hope to catch up later in the evening or at another time altogether.

The meal is divine, and everyone is quite taken with us. Lots of questions are asked about our plans and hopes for the newly formed town of Everton. We are told the history and mythology of the area. Some tall tales I am sure, but it is all very intriguing. We are also told that its wool industry has been hit hard by the depression. When Nate can steal a moment from the bombardment of questions, he leans into me, lightly brushing my ear with his lips and sending a tingle down my spine. He whispers, 'You are very beautiful tonight, Mrs Clintoff, and I would love to take you to a darkened corridor and have my way with you.'

I take my serviette and place it over my mouth, concealing the wicked smile spreading across my lips. I turn to face Nate and he becomes very businesslike: someone must be watching. 'I have learnt far more at this gathering than I have from my superiors at the meetings I've attended leading up to our departure from London, and now Melbourne,' he says. Which is the day after tomorrow. He wonders whether they have been keeping him in the dark so as to not scare him off. Maybe they are right to. If we knew of the true dire-straits situation, would we have come?

The one story that is repeated is to do with the unrest of the natives. Most have been dispersed but there is still a stronghold of the last remaining tribesmen in the Everton area. With the depression reaching and affecting all, there is much crime, theft of livestock and lives lost on both sides in 'payback'. 'Frontier wars' is what Nate calls the unrest.

Of course, all the women gush over Nate and compliment me on my good fortune in being his wife. I tell them it is his good fortune to have me as his wife! There is lots of hidden laughter behind well-placed handkerchiefs as they float away to start other circles of conversation, throwing looks over their shoulders at me. Forced smiles of endearment. Maybe I am too down-to-earth for them, but dammit, I am being me and I won't change for anyone. At least Lady Hopetoun has taken a liking to me.

I head to the ladies' powder room to relieve myself and sit in silence for a moment. I think the journey is finally catching up with me.

Attending to Nate and Samuel with their discomfort at sea and now, once on land, having time for myself, to let my guard down and relax a little, an uneasiness has crept upon me.

The powder room has a quaint little room off to the side for my much-needed purpose, to take the weight off my feet: a divan, hand fans, cool washcloths and cool fresh water. I utilise it well until I hear laughter and idle gossip from the stalls. Two young women are giggling over the flirtatious nature of one of their friends with the handsome British man who is going to run a town in the Snowy Mountains. 'I will have to plan a skiing trip up that way and track him down!' More giggles and carry-on. I promptly exit to find my husband.

One of my downfalls is that I have a tendency to be very jealous. I don't know why, or where it has come from: Nate is my first and only lover. For all the time we have been married I have not felt at all threatened, and as to why I allow that ugly green monster to overwhelm me, I have no idea. But right now, here in a foreign land, in a city where I do not have my Lisbeth for an ally – or any friends, for that matter – the monster will be released to protect what is mine. I march into the ballroom with gusto!

I don't intend to start any trouble, but I am determined to find this young lass and put her in her place. I don't have to look too far. I see almost straight away the band of young, pretty vultures circling my husband. The little blond-haired lass is flirting up a storm, actually placing her hand on Nate's arm. I am quite sure he is only being polite as he holds her gaze. Then he spies me and politely removes her hand, and steps towards me as I reach the circle of lust. Gracious and calm, with nothing to hide, he places his hand in the small of my back. 'Darling, I was wondering where you had got to. This is my beautiful wife ...' – half of them have left the circle by now – '... Louisa Clintoff.' The few that remain curtsey politely, nod and leave.

'Thank God you got here,' Nate whispered urgently. 'That was getting ridiculous.'

'Really?' I say, in a tone far too harsh.

'Yes, Mrs Clintoff. Really.' Nate leans in and kisses me, seductively putting on a show for the young lasses, and I play right along, draping my arm around his neck, staring daggers at the blond one, who cannot hide her disappointment. So much so that I burst out laughing. Nate takes me in his arms and swirls me onto the dance floor.

As we glide together he informs me: 'I was hoping to meet Judge Eisenmangher. He was supposed to be here tonight. He is the presiding judge in the area where Everton is situated and is looking to become mayor, so I was hoping to set up a meeting for tomorrow, get a run-down on his plans. A final briefing from him before we head off would be most welcome, since he really knows the place better than most. I do have his briefing papers, I guess.'

On those papers is a direct order: *Go straight to the southern end of town, last house on the left. For keys to your home and your work premises: office, jail and troopers' quarters. Father McGuinness to give further directions and instructions. Consider him the unofficial mayor of Everton.*

'Speaking of papers, did you get the maps for our travel?' I ask. 'We really need to set some time aside tomorrow to study them. Any lands to avoid?' Dare I say it: 'The unrest with the natives?'

Nate assures me that from his briefings today, it appears as if most of the troublesome blacks have been driven higher up into the mountains. 'The others are content to live at a camp or reserve – newly founded at Cohens Lake, which was renamed Blackfellows Lake.'

Apart from Nate's disappointment in Judge Eisenmangher not being present, and the lusty young leeches latching onto my husband, the night is a great success and we are glad to have attended. But we are both happy with our decision to leave when we do.

Back in our room, with Samuel sound asleep in his cot and the nursemaid dismissed, Nate and I make love. With the stress and tension of our trip over here, and our plans all in place, he can finally release. And release he does.

Nate is a magnificent lover, very caring and gentle but forceful and manly when required. I love our moments of intimacy and I'm not afraid to instigate our lovemaking, either. Nate gave me that permission long ago. It's all right for a woman to have these desires. He cares to make me satisfied. I dare not ask how he knows how to do this, and I don't care – I'm just grateful for his efforts and that he is mine.

Our naked, sweaty bodies glide over each other with ease, hands exploring, driven by the desire to please. His arm muscles bulge under the strain of keeping himself raised above me as he thrusts, throwing his head back, burying his manhood deep inside me. Our thrusts are strong but measured. We are in no rush tonight. We both know we will be on the road for a week at least, living rough under the stars, no comfort of a soft bed – although the thought of nature, being naked in the wild, excites me. But tonight, here and now, we enjoy our creature comforts and relish in our lovemaking. Something has ignited in Nate and the pleasure is all mine.

Louisa fulfils me in more ways than one. With a woman I love and admire, my sexual desire and needs mean so much more these days. I am blessed and grateful. And I can't hold on much longer but the desire in her glazed eyes cautions me to wait as I know she is close – we are both close – and tonight we will climax as one. I bury my face in the curve of her neck because her eyes are driving me wild. But her scent and then her gasp of ecstasy push me over the edge. I thrust deep as she lifts her hips to meet me and finally, together, we finish in one lustful loving moment. A smile of sheer contentment grows on her lips and I melt into her, relishing in our afterglow. We exhale together. We kiss and separate, but I drag her into me and we cuddle, her bottom pressing firmly into me, perfectly. We fit together as pieces in a puzzle do, a hand in a glove. And before long we both drift off to sleep.

FIVE

Two weeks earlier, Snowy Mountains

Moss-covered granite boulders display a beautiful contrast in texture of softness and hardness. A precise depiction of this land and my world, the harshness of my life cushioned by the unconditional love of my children. From the recent rain, the moss's bright green on the black-grey granite is stark, contrastin' with the snow-white trunks of the white sallees scattered on the hillside. Yellowing tufts of tussock grass, indicating autumn is upon us, jut out from the boulders and rocks that form the cavernous walls to the river below, its dark water indicatin' its depth.

My hands are red raw. I keep hittin' the blasted rock. Don't know why I bother – if I scrub any harder these blasted clothes will fall apart in my bare hands. They are not far from being called rags. But the washin' needs to be done. It's been rainin' nonstop for a full week. The rain came from the north. Dark clouds loomed over the northern ranges for a whole week before landin' and dumpin' on us. Last of the significant autumn rains.

Today is the first time the sun has shone, and the children are covered in mud. They didn't even have to go outside. The roof is in urgent need of repair. The slat-wall gaps need refillin' and my once-hard dirt floor has become a mud pit. Rain from all directions. So, this mornin' up early, usin' the mud and a *Woman's Journal*, me and the children start to pack the gaps in the walls.

I get the journals from a peddler. He used to come out once in a blue moon but he doesn't come much anymore, none of them do, they know I can't afford to buy anythin'. They're usually old issues by the time I get them, but I don't mind. I like to read; Miss Shirley instilled this in me. 'But don't be too forward about it,' she cautioned. The journals are an outlet and connection to the world beyond my little home, so isolated up here in the mountains. And a learnin' tool for the children. They can all read and write, I made sure of that. Beside their schoolin' purpose, the journals come in handy as gap fillers and toilet paper.

I gave the children instructions the night before: 'When ya's get up, have a little breakfast. There's damper there, dip it in some black tea – ya can have a bit of sugar in ya's tea this mornin'. Then I need ya's to gather some sweetgrass.' I lay this grass on the muddy floor to soak up the moisture.

Molly lies sleeping, content, a little extra sleep-in a very rare pleasure. A long, soft hessian pillow rests under her belly and between her knees. Her breathing is gentle and even. She is woken by laughter. Her children are rolling over the sweetgrass to help smooth out the muddy footprints in the once perfectly kept dirt floor, helping to soak up the excess water. It's how she gets them to do their chores without too much fuss: turn everything into a game. The children love doing this; they love getting the mud all over themselves. Laughter and giggles sure beat the bickering and squabbling of the past few days.

Washday is always a full day. Clothes and bodies to wash and dry. Put the traps in for food. If an emu nest is found along the way, maybe steal an egg but never two, and then time to play, wear the children out. Home to eat the catch of the day and then to bed. Molly knows if she leaves the doors and window slats open while they are away for washday, the floor will dry and harden a little before their return.

Winter is coming, and washing in the river gets too cold to bare. It'll be back to washcloth and hot water off the stove or the hot springs; they're a short walk from the property. But she saves the hot springs for her own pleasure. She doesn't have many pleasurable moments in her life besides the joy of her children, so when she can steal a moment she enjoys this little indulgence. She shared the springs with Danny when he was a baby and of course Delphi – a mother–daughter moment. But the hot springs are hers, and hers alone.

As they head off down the back, Danny carries a homemade fish trap. 'Remind me to get some wattle on the way back. Did you bring the tins?' asks Molly.

Joe Junior holds up four tins that once held rosella jam, tropical fruit and candied peel from the Hargreaves cannery in Brisbane that Joe brought back from a drove to Queensland. They have wire as homemade handles. 'Best time after rain for the wattle, eh Ma?' chimes in Henry James, a scrawny little fellow with hair that has a mind of its own. It sticks out in all directions, wiry like his da's.

'Yes, son.' Molly smiles down at her usually nonverbal son. Joe Junior does all the talking for his little brother. Those two are thick as thieves, little rascals but good kids in general.

Wattle gum was a treat her father would give her. A gin showed him how and when to collect it, and with a sprinkle of sugar, when he had it, or stole a pocketful, it made for a nice treat. Molly remembers as a little girl once demanding her da remove his pants so she could lick his pockets clean of sugar. There were holes in each pocket, so most of the sugar he'd stolen had been lost to the road on his walk home. But she licked the last of it from the cloth. So when she can spare it, she adds a pinch of white gold to give it a little sweetness, a nice dessert, but only if the children have behaved, and only a little. You can't have too much of the wattle gum or you'll get a bellyache. Not a good thing to be dealing with when the *Woman's Journal*s are all used up on gap filler for the walls.

Molly thinks, her face frowning a little, *Hopefully we'll get some fish, that will do for dinner tonight.* Cupboards are bare, so the catch is needed.

As they reach the river, the boys jump from boulder to boulder. The banks are low and close enough for the jumping game. The boulders are majestic, so impressive you wonder how they got there and were placed where they lie. Her da once told her, his Scottish accent strong, that God must have put them there: *He was playin' marbles with his disciples.* At another time, Molly told her children the countryside was once a land of giants, and just as they used small rocks to make structures, so did the giants' children with the boulders.

The valley where this river runs would have once been filled with a massive volume of water; its high cavernous walls indicate this. And where Molly and the children wash the clothes and bathe there is a deep swimming hole. The land opens up and there's a bank for convenience. Granite covered in moss and white sallees form the backdrop.

Now about eight months along, Molly's pregnant belly makes washing awkward today. She sits back on her haunches, releasing the pain in her back, and sighs deeply. But the noise of her children arguing breaks her concentration. She turns to face her boys, bathing in the shallows a little further downriver. 'Enough, you boys. Don't wanna hear it. Sort it.'

Danny, Joe Junior and Henry James fall silent, their heads hung low. 'Not today, boys. We've been cooped up in that house all week because of that blasted rain, and I listened to ya fightin' and carryin' on, and I just don't wanna hear it. Ya's can get out now and dry off.'

The boys get out of the water reluctantly with a final push and shove and, under their breaths, a final blame. Each wears worn yellowing britches, patches dominating the original fabric. Delphi looks up at her brothers from where she's playing on the bank, a cheeky grin on her face. All siblings like it when the others get in trouble. But whatever the boys have been fighting about is short-lived. New ideas for a game are passed between them as they head further downriver to the big boulders.

Molly's worn hands gather up the wet clothes. She steadies herself and heaves to get up from the ground, her upper body the last thing to come upright. She grunts with the last exertion, then takes the washed clothes and hangs them on small shrubs nearby. Their brittle branches stab at her pregnant belly, breaking off as she reaches to spread out each item of clothing. Once done, she stretches her back and waddles over to a nearby tree. She sits, her hands finding the trunk behind her for support and guidance to the ground. Her back rests in a groove in the trunk. 'Be careful. Play safe. Stay close. No yellin' and watch out for ya sister.'

Cute as a button, Delphi plays by the water's edge with her rag doll and makes mud cakes for a tea party. She is in a world of her own, lost in her imagination. Oblivious to what is going on around her.

'I'm havin' a nap. And I don't wanna be woke until I wake,' Molly tells the children.

They all chime, 'Yes, Ma.'

Molly settles back into the tree. *Every part of my body aches today. I'm exhausted. This baby is drainin' the livin' daylights out of me.* It has been a trying few days with the constant wet weather and four young, bored, hungry children. Sleep comes fast. A few deep inhales and Molly's breathing becomes gentle and rhythmic as she nods off.

Delphi is engrossed in making her mud cakes. Her rag doll lies dangerously close to the water's edge. The water laps at it. Delphi pats at the cakes, then stops and is intrigued as she takes a closer look. They are moving, wriggling. The little girl's face fills with a frown of curiosity. The mud wriggles and the cakes lose their shape. She pats at them, trying to get them back to their roundness. Did she add too much water to her mix of mud and broken twigs? She stops and there it is again: they wriggle.

Delphi looks to concur with her rag doll, but it is gone. It floats out in the murky brown *flood*water! The river's current has picked up in pace and volume and there is a distant rumbling, a cracking and tearing. Delphi becomes upset as she watches her dolly floating away. She looks towards her brothers and calls, 'Danny?' and points at the doll floating towards them.

Molly sleeps, but her eyelids begin to flicker. Has she heard Delphi? Has she felt the rumbling? Her face distorts: she is dreaming. Her eyelids continue to flicker as she tries to make sense of the impressionistic jumbled images, too obscure to see details, flashing before her mind's eye. Her breathing becomes shallow and quick. Her hands tense, grabbing at her dress over her pregnant belly. She mumbles something inaudible. The rumbling sound is getting louder and closer. The roar of her surroundings cuts through her nightmare and she sits bolt upright, looking around to get her bearings.

Then she sees it. In the now-swollen river a massive boulder, well over six feet in height, rolls with the rushing floodwater. That's what is causing the tremor, the cracking and tearing, taking out anything that stands in its way. Her children's anxious voices are calling, cutting through the roar of the raging water. Molly scrambles to her feet, stumbling over her long-tattered dress skirt. She pulls Delphi back from the river's edge. 'Move away! Further up the bank!' Delphi does as she is told. 'Stay there.'

Standing on the bank of the river, they are stilled by the shock of what they see. The browning floodwater is flushing down from upstream, from further north, after all the heavy rains over the past few weeks. It is swirling around the base of the boulders where the boys stand. Joe Junior points to the floodwater: 'Snuck up on us, Ma!'

'Get off the boulders and onto the bank! Now!' The boys do as they are told. They understand the urgency in their ma's voice, and they know the ways of Mother Nature: floodwater comes quick and fast. Then Molly realises Danny is not with them. She calls to them: 'Danny! Where's Danny?'

I snap my head up and down the river looking for my eldest. The murky brown floodwater camouflages him. Danny's olive skin and sandy-coloured hair are lost in the rapidly risin' water. Then I see where the other two are lookin' and pointin'. With just the tips of his fingers, Danny clings to a boulder. The violent force of the water helps to keep him there. There is debris, a fallen tree from a previous flood, caught between two other boulders. This is probably savin' Danny from bein' swept away. He holds Delphi's rag doll in his mouth and is hangin' on for dear life. Time has slowed now. If I was a Christain I would thank the Lord. I whip my head around to see the massive boulder slowly inchin' its way downriver, causing a wave of turbulent whitewash that builds as it moves. The boulder is on a direct collision course with Danny.

My frantic panic subsides and clarity arrives. I scream, 'Hang on, Danny! Hang on, son!' And then I plunge into the fast-movin' water but I slip . . . I reach out. I grasp at the water. No stablilty, I fall and I'm quickly swept along with the current and forced under. *No. No!*

Molly's three other children huddle together. They have worked their way up to Delphi. They look at where their mother has gone under, then glance at Danny. The boulder is almost upon him. He braces himself for the impact, knowing he's in trouble. He will be crushed. But just as the boulder rolls towards him, it hits something under the water and is turned ever so slightly. It collides with the debris, crushing it, breaking it into twigs, freeing it. In pieces the tree floats away, taking Danny with it. Delphi lets out a blood-curdling scream that bounces around the mountain range and echoes back to slap the reality of this nightmare into each of their little faces. She knows this is all her fault. Tears spill from her eyes. Her little lips tremble.

Under the water I have lost all orientation, I don't know where up or down is. I need to find it soon. My lungs are burnin'. I try. Dammit, I'm tryin' to find the surface but I am bein' tossed around like a rag doll myself. I'm bein' stabbed at by debris under the water and debris that floats on the surface. I try to protect my belly, my unborn baby . . . *oh, no – my unborn baby.* Then I am snagged by a branch. It brings me to a joltin' halt and for a second, I see where 'up' is. I kick with all my might to swim to the surface but I can't move – the tree branch has a tight hold on my skirt. I'm frantic now. I twist and turn, trying to break the branch or rip the material from it, but the movement only winds my dress tighter. My lungs scream for oxygen; my mind cries for my children. *Danny!*

I have no choice but to try and breathe, not that I want to open my mouth but it's what my brain is tellin' my body to do, that's how you breathe, and by compulsion my mouth gapes open and I breathe in ... water! I pull at my dress but it refuses to give. I take in more water, my body starts to reject it, my mind ... suddenly becomes composed. I flutter my eyes to find focus.

There before me ... floatin' before me ... is a woman. A fair-skinned Aboriginal woman, her native features strong in the contours of her face, her hair red; long and swirlin' with the current like the velvet-green weed stuck between the river rocks. She looks to be about twenty-seven years old. A calmness comes over me. I'm mesmerised by the woman's deep, dark eyes. I stare at her as if nothing else matters. The look in her eyes tells me something, I tilt my head to understand her thoughts. She speaks to me ... her eyes wide, knowing ... she is willing me on. To fight. To live. My children! I reach for the Aboriginal woman just as the branch my dress is entwined on breaks.

I am quickly swept away and the Aboriginal woman is gone too. Only a small piece of material remains, ripplin' with the movement of the current.

Later that night, reused worn-down candles sit on the kitchen table. They light the wall behind, where a wooden plaque is mounted. The family name, *JOHNSON*, is burnt into it and decorated with a child's attempts at flowers and stars.

At the table beneath the plaque, Joe Junior, Henry James and Delphi sit quietly, tear-stained. In the distance they hear the cry of the powerful owl. He's a little early with his calling: he's not usually heard until winter. Delphi wipes her runny nose with the back of her hand.

A noise grabs Joe Junior's attention and he looks over to the bedroom, the other room in the shanty.

There, his ma and brother, both looking deathly pale, are lying side by side on a large homemade stretcher-bed, branches for bedposts and wooden slats for the base under a lumpy old hessian mattress. Two single stretcher-beds line the walls. The children share these.

Delphi tries to speak through little sobs: 'Is Ma and Danny gonna wake soon? I want them to wake up now.'

'They're just restin'. They've had a bad day.' Wise words from a young soul.

Finally, Molly stirs. The children at the table sit upright with anticipation. In her slumber Molly throws an arm over Danny, cradling her precious eldest son. She murmurs something inaudible, then her breathing settles to an even rhythm.

A hungry stomach growls. Delphi places her hand over her belly. 'Excuse me,' she apologises politely.

Joe Junior looks at her, knowing there is nothing to eat. He gets up all the same, hoping by some miracle there is food in the cupboard. On the shelves there is only a small amount of flour in a calico sack. He goes to the vegetable box: nothing. He opens the lid of the meat box: nothing in there either. Henry James joins him, peering into the empty meat box. 'Has it been three months yet?'

'Not sure what three months is. I guess it might be.'

They move over to the stove that sits in the big old river-rock chimney. It's the only real, solid structural mass in the shanty. If a big gust of wind came through, it would blow the rest of the shack away. But while their abode is run-down, despite the dire conditions it is quaint and homely. It's clear that Molly has tried to make it a home, but the room is bare of any indulgences. A table and chairs, a cupboard for food and a utility cupboard line one wall. The stove is at one end and on the other wall the veggie and meat boxes sit, as well as a small bench for preparing food.

The rag doll that caused all the chaos hangs over Molly's makeshift rocking chair, drying. The boys sit on the dirt floor, which has managed to dry to a reasonable firmness. Delphi joins them, fitting snugly between her brothers. 'If the three months is up, that means the baby be here soon,' she says.

Joe Junior nods at his little sister and Henry James adds, 'And Da be home, with supplies. We'll eat good then, Delphi.'

Delphi rubs at her hungry belly, which makes another little noise. 'But I'm hungry now.' Joe Junior gently places a caring arm around his little sister, the only comfort he can offer.

The children stare at the stove that does not provide for them tonight. It's going to be a long night on empty stomachs.

The sun hangs high in a cloudless sky. Danny, a little gaunt, sits in the dirt, focused on writing his name; he prides himself on his penmanship, although he writes with his finger. He wishes he had a notepad to preserve his efforts.

Delphi, who is never too far from her big brother, sits beside him playing with her rag doll. She rubs its tummy and holds the doll to her ear, as if it is whispering to her. Delphi looks down at her rag doll with empathy: 'You shouldn't talk about how hungry you are. That only makes it worse.' She gets up and takes her doll over to play by the old snow gum.

Joe Junior and Henry James play on the woodheap out the front. It's low on wood. A mound protrudes beneath it, making the ground uneven. Just beyond it is the old snow gum where Delphi and her doll play. The snow gum marks the end of the cleared area of the front yard.

Beyond that are perfectly placed white sallees marking the perimeter of Molly's property, and beyond these trees are further young saplings, scrub and thicket; the land then drops away to the river below. To the left, the south, are the flood plains. You can see the river stretch out before you, snaking its way through the land. But due to the ridge and the trees, perfectly placed boulders and thicket, Molly's home is hidden. She has the advantage of seeing who is coming, but any visitor has to get lost to find her. Just the way she likes it. Isolated from the world.

Giggles and ruckus can be heard from the two younger boys, who are lost in their game of jumping on the mound of dirt under the dwindling woodheap. Delphi happily plays quietly with her doll. Danny continues to write his name in the dirt. He is extra-sombre this morning, and rightly so. He experienced a great ordeal yesterday and is still a little shaken up. He rewrites his name in the damp earth, claiming his place here on dry land. Making his mark in this life, perhaps.

Molly lies in bed, staring at the gaps in her slat roof. The streams of sunlight shining through the cracks have disturbed her slumber. She wipes at a tear that falls down her cheek. Is she crying, or is it the glare from the sunlight? She rolls over and closes her eyes, allowing the tears to fall freely. She can't help herself. Molly Johnson rarely cries, but her face distorts with the pain of yesterday, the fear that ran through her as she fought the raging river, wondering whether she would ever see her children again. But her cries are unheard, her silent screams only for her. She doesn't want to alarm the children. A practice she's done many times before. After a moment, as quickly as the crying started, it stops. There is no one to hear, no one to confide in or to comfort her. No one cares, so why bother? 'Cryin' gets ya nowhere' is what her da always said.

Molly slowly lifts herself from the bed and wipes her tears away with the back of her hand, wipes her nose with the hem of her dress.

She takes another moment and pushes up from the bed, then slowly makes her way to the front door. Her worry is replaced with calm and strength as she nears the opening. Her mind moves forward to today, this very moment, to be here in the present and so happy to be there. She's had her time to dwell on what could have been; now, it's time to hatch a plan for how to get through this day. But her relief is short-lived as she realises she is not well. Her body aches, as it should from what she has been through, but this pain is deep, in her joints, and Molly realises she has a fever. *Oh dear, this is all I need – a sickness from the water I swallowed in the flood.*

Molly leans against the doorframe. In the light of day, she looks exhausted and pale. She is certainly unwell – she can't hide that. Her pregnant belly is prominent as her undergarments, wet from fever, cling to her. 'You two boys get away from that woodheap. Not gonna tell ya's again. Get around back and play.'

Henry James and Joe Junior scamper off, giggling. *Little rascals*, Molly thinks. Her attention falls on her eldest son. 'Danny, you up to ridin' to the McGuinnesses'?'

Danny doesn't look up. He finishes the word, his name, again.

'Danny?'

He punctuates his finish with a full stop, burying his finger in the soft earth, frustrated, angry. He would never truly let his ma see this side of him; it is very rare that he rebels or disrespects an order from her. Knowing it's his job to see his brothers and sister safely to the McGuinnesses' when Molly is due to give birth, he says, 'Don't look like ya drop enough yet, Ma.'

Molly can't help but smile, her hand gliding over her pregnant belly. Her son is far beyond his years. 'For food, son,' she tells him.

Danny doodles in the dirt, not too eager to move. 'Everton's not just over the hill, Ma.'

'I know it's a long way to town, son.'

Molly looks to the woodheap again and exhales deeply. Danny hears this and understands his ma's worry. 'We need to fell a tree,' she says. 'The dead wood isn't gonna last us the winter.'

He gets up, dusting off the seat of his pants, but the moisture in the soil stains his bottom. 'I'll get to that, too.'

He heads around the back, looking for his dog. 'Alligator!'

But the big black mixed-breed he found as a half-starved little puppy doesn't come running. The dog's been away before, but not this long. Danny calls again, louder this time, and his voice echoes, bouncing off the vast mountain range: 'Alligator!'

But no dog comes running.

Stepping high through the clusters of browning tussock grass, he can hear his ma coughing violently as she heads back inside. *Blasted dog*, Danny thinks as he gathers the horse's saddle blanket and bridle from a little lean-to shed at the side of the yard. He approaches the wood-fence holding yard, slipping under the top rail. The yard is in urgent need of repair. If the grey speckled mare wasn't so faithful, she could have easily stepped over the broken rails and walked off. She can often be found out of the yard, and after eating her fill of fresh grass will walk herself back in for the night. Dimples is their only form of transport into town for supplies, errands or help. She is a valued and much-loved family member.

And there she is, the old mare, the family's faithful workhorse, standing in the yard, her back swayed from the weight of carrying children and supplies over the years. She would sometimes accompany Joe on his droves up to the high country carrying supplies; he would later set her loose and she would immediately find her way home. Today the animal's head hangs low. Danny takes no notice: he is preoccupied with his annoyance about going to town and wondering where his blasted dog is. As he nears Dimples, he mumbles swear words under his breath that he would never say loud enough for his ma to hear. She doesn't like it when he cusses: he sounds too much like his da.

Danny throws the blanket over the back of the horse, and her legs buckle. He jumps back out of harm's way as she hits the ground, hard, with a final expiration of air from her nostrils and arse. The boy is left standing there, stunned and staring at the dead animal. He looks at the horse's head and sees that her mouth is swollen and has two puncture marks highlighted by blood. Danny squats beside her for a closer inspection. Snake bite. He runs his hand through her mane, offering soft solemn words of thanks. He affectionately pats the head of their faithful mare, perplexed as to what to do now. With food so low and his ma close to giving birth, how the hell are they gonna get to town? How is he going to manage to get the others to the McGuinnesses' when his ma's ready to give birth? She always sends them in. Gives her rest and some quiet bonding time with the baby.

This is my fault, Danny thinks. *I shouldn't have been swearin'.* He sits back from the dead horse. *Blast it, I'm gonna have to dig a bloody hole to bury the bastard.*

Danny hugs his knees. In the light of day, the land around him and his family is of heroic proportions. The colossal mountain range stretches to the north and south and the thick scrub country dwarfs Molly and her children isolated within it, danger anywhere and everywhere. A crow circles once, twice, three times then flies off towards the mountain range, up and over.

Six

Over the mountain range lies another property that belongs to a family with money: the Edwards. Cleared land. Neatly cut hedges mark the perimeter of a red-brick homestead and manicured lawn.

The Edwards family were among the first white settlers in the area and are considered among the founding fathers. They came to the high country in the early 1820s looking for more land to graze their livestock. The patriarch, Charles, led the trip with his youngest son, Neville, and five other men, leaving his mother, Evelyn, wife, Florence, and daughter-in-law, Eleanor, with their hired help – a simpleton boy of about seventeen years old – to help with any manual labour.

These white men befriended the local Ngarigo tribe and learnt about the land from these original inhabitants. King Jimmy, a name given to the head elder of the Ngarigo by the troopers who had passed through the outpost of Cresthill in the valley below, fell under the spell of the good-natured, sweet-talking, gift-giving Charles Edwards. And the Ngarigo elder showed the white men the hidden tracks of the high country that were invisible to the untrained eye.

The Ngarigo had ancient connections to this country, dating back to when time began. They were intrigued by the white man they had heard about. Other nations and tribes who gathered for the bogong moth celebrations brought stories, songs and dances about their encounters with the pale-skinned beings, who were first thought to be lost relatives returning to them from the clouds. That story soon changed: the pale-skins could not be trusted, and any business with them must be undertaken with caution. But when the leading elder of the Ngarigo saw the white men with his own eyes, he was astounded and intrigued at their pale skin, many shades of coloured hair and eyes, and the cloth that covered their bodies from neck to foot. They smelt. And some had body shapes that looked wrong to the Ngarigo.

This kind would hold up the tribe, the elder thought, examining an overweight stockman. He would be considered sickly, and would be left behind. The Ngarigo elder thought that the pale-skins' elder needed a stern talking-to about the care of his clan, but it was not his place to impose his values and conditions on others. It was all very intriguing. To the Ngarigo they were the superior and for their amusement, they toyed with the out-of-shape harmless pale-skins and obliged their inquiries. Talk was passed around about the cloth that covered their pale bodies: 'Are these pale creatures ashamed to show their masculinity and their athletic prowess?' The Ngarigo weren't even sure that they were men – they could not see their male appendage. 'The others who are soft could be the females?' was one comment. Laughter was shared as they attempted to lift the round belly of one of the more mature men, which hung over his long loincloth. They were looking for his *dhun*, his penis. The stockman backed away, shaking his head, waving his arms in defence. The Ngarigo men then thought that he must be a woman.

The high country was breathtakingly beautiful – the perfect place, the whites nodded in agreement, to graze their sheep and fatten them up before the winter sales. The Ngarigo thought the white men were agreeing with them on the beauty of the place, understanding the Ngarigo's connection to the land through complex songlines crossing this country, and its plentiful edible plant life that had sustained them for many, many years.

But the two groups of men didn't know or understand that, with each of their respective head nods, they were agreeing to totally different things. This misunderstanding was the start of the demise and destruction of the area. And this destruction did not just mean the plant life.

Charles Edwards, his son Neville and the other men stayed for a few nights in the area with the blacks, thinking them childish, naive and uneducated in the ways of the civilised Western world. The Ngarigo thought of the pale creatures as dismal beings, not schooled in the ancient lore of their great land. King Jimmy said, 'I would like to educate these beings in our ways so they can appreciate our knowledge of the land and sky, and the ways of our clans.' Most of the Ngarigo men did not see the sense in this, and hoped the white men would just look and leave.

They shared a meal of kangaroo, and the pale-skin with the hanging round belly was given one of King Jimmy's wives. She led him into a *goongee* and, not long after, came running out, half laughing but also a little scared. As she scampered by King Jimmy she said, 'The round-belly one is a *marinj*. He has a *dhun*, it's old. Small one, too.' All the Ngarigo roared with laughter. The whites were left bewildered and wondering.

Unfortunately for the Ngarigo women, the white men could not help but be drawn to their beauty, shining in the moonlight: their fresh, young pointed breasts; pouting, soft, full lips; small waists and high buttocks; and long, well-shaped legs. With the full moon's beams bouncing off the women's velvet-black skin, the white men found it hard to resist their primal urges. But their greed and pompous sense of entitlement led to brutal rapes. The white men demanded silence, holding the Ngarigo women against their will at knife and gun point as the taking began.

The whites' brutality against the Ngarigo women quickly caused unrest among the Ngarigo men. A young Ngarigo warrior came for his wife to find her crying, scratch marks on her shoulders and buttocks and her mouth bleeding. She told her husband through sobs of pain and shame what had happened. The youngest white man had taken her against her will: 'He acted like a *dulugal*. A wild man with no control or care.' He had bitten down on her voluptuous lips, drawing blood, and clawed at her like the wombat digging his burrow. Angered, the young warrior immediately summoned the others and told them what he had learnt. They held council and a decision was made to confront the white men and demand punishment for their acts – but they were long gone.

Charles knew about his youngest son's sexual fetish. Neville rarely showed this side, but when he did, it was Charles who coughed up money to soften the blows on the prostitutes Neville bit and bruised. Charles never said a word to anyone about it, especially Neville's new wife. To take out his disgusting urges on a gin was safer than revealing his deviant sexual ways to Eleanor, the beautiful young woman from Melbourne he'd made his wife. Charles didn't want her running off until an heir had been born.

But Charles Edwards carried great sins of his own. He also took a young Aboriginal girl by force that night. She was about fourteen years old and, unbeknown to Charles, the youngest promised wife to King Jimmy. She was a virgin and became pregnant to Charles. When the baby was born with fine features and fair skin, King Jimmy wanted her killed immediately. He felt she was a bad omen for the tribe and its clans, and that his young wife had deceived him. He did not entirely blame her for this. Stories of the treatment of the young warrior's wife and those told by others who had finally come forward suggested to King Jimmy his young wife would not have wanted to go willingly with the out-of-shape, smelly pale-skin.

But her mixed-blood baby was another story. Was it fit enough to be part of the clan? Was it weaker because of its tainted blood? The young Aboriginal mother had no choice but to leave the newborn out under her birthing tree on the night she was born. She asked the ancient ancestors to watch over the baby girl and give her strength to survive the night. If she survived, she would be considered strong enough to be included in the clan.

The next morning before dawn the young mother went to her baby and found her alive and well. She had triumphantly survived the night. The baby girl was named Waraganj after the snow-gum tree under which she had been born.

Some in the tribe, mainly King Jimmy's other wives, did not like it: they thought the young mother useless to allow herself to become with child to the pale-skinned intruder. So they banished her and her daughter. Waraganj and her young mother drifted on the outskirts of the tribe for a few years until the mother returned to the clan showing her swollen pregnant belly and demanded a place beside King Jimmy and his other wives because she was now carrying his child. The tribe finally let her and her two-year-old daughter back in.

Waraganj was soon promised to another tribesman from one of the coastal clans. Sixteen winters passed and then her time came – she was to go to him. She gathered her things and was due to start her journey to his country the next morning, but instead of going with him, she ran – from the tribe, her clan, her mother, her younger siblings, and the protection her extended family could offer her.

From a young age she'd had a curious mind and an adventurous and rebellious spirit. Her mother and siblings blamed her tainted blood for her rebellion against lore, but they loved her dearly. She often made them laugh when she played the clown at storytime. And as one of the most skilled dancers in the clan, she made her family proud. Her red hair, fair skin and finer features made her rather exotic-looking, and the young warriors lusted after her – but she could not help the way she looked. She paid them no heed and kept her virtue intact and her self-respect high. But she always felt she was an outsider. The other women in the clan would taunt her with their sharp-tongued insults. Life for Waraganj within the tribe would have been a different story if she'd been King Jimmy's flesh and blood.

The night she ran away, Waraganj served her promised husband his meal, and sat with him through council with King Jimmy and then with her mother to talk. For a long while she just held her mother's hand as they sat around the family fire and watched the younger siblings tell of their day's adventures through song and dance, roaring with laughter at some of their unfortunate mishaps. When the others, including her promised husband, went off to their *goongees* to sleep, Waraganj asked if her mother would stay with her a little longer. They sat in silence for a few moments more, then Waraganj opened up about a dream she'd had.

In the dream she stood on a cliff in her promised husband's land, raging water beneath her, calling as the waves reached up and splashed at her feet. She felt the full weight of this new world crushing her chest and taking her breath away. And she fought hard to breathe again. Her mother reassured her that this was a normal feeling but Waraganj continued, giving no heed to the words of her *njadjan*, her mother.

'There is a path to this side, on the side where my heart lies. It leads me away, *Njadjan*.' There was instant fear in her mother's eyes. 'It led away and back down the cliff. It was narrow and dangerously close to the edge, rugged with big boulders, but it kept going for a long, long way off into the distance, *Njadjan*.'

Waraganj explained to her mother that the narrow path with the obstacles was her path to take, and she had to leave. She would not go to her promised husband. Together they cried – this could bring death to Waraganj. They held each other tight, her *njadjan* knowing that she could not say anything that would change her daughter's mind.

'For your safety, Waraganj, I will not raise the alarm until well after the sun has risen.' Waraganj held her mother knowing this was the last time she would feel her *njadjan*'s warmth, safety and care, squeezing her tight and showing her thanks for her understanding. Looking deep into her soul, Waraganj's *njadjan* said, 'My love for you is as ancient as this land. As beautiful as a flittering butterfly, and forever joyous as a bubbling spring. Always know it is me in the rustle of the leaves of treetops. Watching. Following.'

Waraganj didn't know how to respond to her mother's beautiful words, but she tried her best. 'My love for you is as pure as the first opening of a wildflower in spring. My love for you is forever as a blue sky on a summer's day. It will be strong and survive like the cavernous rocky walls that have shaped and still guide the great river. You gave me life. You willed me to live. You stood by me. And *Njadjan*, the choice I make tonight and my action that will take me from here are because you believe in me. I'm a fighter – I've been fighting all my life, and I will not stop fighting until my last breath. Stay safe, *Njadjan*. Stay well.'

I take my mother's face gently in my hands, wiping the tears from her eyes. I kiss her on both cheeks, breathing in her scent one last time. *Njadjan* clenches a fist, steadying me with a firm grasp on my arm, then touches her fist softly to my forehead. As she has done for as long as

I can remember, she blows through it, whispering, 'Always with you.' This alone gives me strength and determination. I slip quietly away into the night. There is no full moon to guide me, perfect for an unseen escape. No moonbeams to highlight my pale skin.

What Waraganj failed to see as she left was her mother's heartbreak. And she never knew that three days after her leaving, her *njadjan*'s broken heart gave way. Waraganj's mother was found sleeping eternally under a beautiful old snow gum. The old gum's trunk, still glistening from rainfall, filled the valley with a rainbow of colour.

Times were getting tough for the Ngarigo and their neighbouring nations. More white people were coming and taking land, putting up fences, driving the blacks away and off their homelands. They were not free to live with the changing seasons as they once had. They now lived to survive, and stayed out of sight. By their own law the white men had the right to shoot any black on sight – to eradicate, or to *disperse*, the heathen savages: 'The blacks cannot and will not hold up the forward progress of building this nation. We will disperse them. For Queen and country, we will prevail.'

Charles Edwards was a regular at these district meetings and often led the discussions. He was the first to propose that the outpost Cresthill be marked for possible development in the near future. If the troopers could disperse the blacks, a town for the area could be considered. 'There is already a major stock route that cuts through, and with more farmers and settlers arriving, a town would do well here,' Charles offered up at many a meeting. He went even further to say that he would help to finance the development of the town, but added, 'The blacks need to be managed.'

A consensus was sanctioned, and unfortunately for the clans of the alpine country, what these white men agreed upon was applied with great haste.

Sleeping under the stars and living off the land, Waraganj ran for many days and nights from both blacks and whites. The clan sent warriors, but they didn't search too far as it was too dangerous, and King Jimmy said she wasn't worth the trouble. He blamed her mother's death on Waraganj leaving and shaming her mother by not going with her promised husband. He added that if she ever returned, she would face the consequences.

Eventually Waraganj came across a homestead. She was astounded at the vast size of this *goongee* and its materials of red brick, which she hadn't seen before. For a moment she thought she might have run straight off her country into another world.

She approached the building with caution and a woman a few years older than her own mother came from inside, dressed in cloth that covered her body from neck to foot. It looked as if she were floating. Had Waraganj died in her sleep and entered the lands of the spirits? And because of her tainted blood had she not gone to the promised lands of the Dreaming but to the hell of the white man? Waraganj burst out crying and fell to her knees, beating her head with sorrow.

My daughter-in-law, Eleanor, asked me to come to the window to see – someone was approaching! My first thought was that it was a white woman in grave trouble – her clothing was tattered and torn, her long red hair wild as a bushfire. The way the poor thing was taking in her surrounds I was sure her mind was gone. When she fell to the ground and began to beat her head, I was quite convinced the woman was deranged. I was fearful to go outside but thought perhaps a gentle, soft, caring female voice could help. I gave Eleanor a pistol and told her to use it if the woman should turn on me.

'Florence, please, I am not the best shot,' Eleanor protested.

From out of nowhere came my mother-in-law, Evelyn. She sternly takes the pistol, cocks it with a knowledge I was not aware of and nods to me, 'Off you go. Keep the woman on your right so I have a clear shot.' As I stepped steadily towards the woman, I realised she was a black – well, her features gave that impression but her skin was a grey-white sprinkled with freckles. I had heard of white men lying with the gins, so this woman was obviously the outcome of the act. Mixed blood. The genes of the white man dominant.

By the time she stopped wailing, Evelyn, Eleanor and I were standing before her and she began to tell us what happened. She did not speak English, which surprised me considering her skin colour. I assumed she was from one of the surrounding homesteads, some of which took in the blacks for labour. They were skilled with the animals.

So through sign language, movement and drawing in the dirt, Waraganj told her heartbreaking story: her fear of being treated unfairly by her new husband and the other women because of her fair skin and tainted blood. Eleanor was appalled and sought permission then and there from Evelyn to let the black girl stay and be a housemaid.

Waraganj hoped she had finally found shelter and acceptance at this homestead with this family: the Edwards family. The elderly woman looked down at her and, as if she had a bad taste in her mouth, spat, 'She'll bring trouble.' She turned and left. But Eleanor was determined to make this young woman her responsibility, and stood her ground.

Unknown to Waraganj, these women were legitimately her family. The oldest woman, the matriarch, Evelyn, was her grandmother. The middle-aged woman, Florence, was Waraganj's stepmother, and Eleanor, who befriended her very quickly, was actually her sister-in-law – the wife of her half-brother, Neville. This was Waraganj's white family. Her father's family. Charles Edwards' family.

Eleanor Markland had married Charles's only surviving son, Neville, the youngest of his and Florence's four children. The eldest son, Charles Junior, had died in a farming accident, and the other son, Phillip, had died two days after his birth. An older daughter, Mavis, was always sickly and died not long after she was married; the talk was she took her own life. And the younger daughter, Bertha, married and moved to Perth, on the other side of Australia. She was slow to bring grandchildren into the world, and her interests were in Western Australia, not the Snowy Mountains.

Waraganj managed to settle in at the Edwards' homestead easily. She liked it there with the three women who appeared to run the property, the boss women. She understood that if she worked hard and was obedient, she would be looked after. Eleanor taught her to speak English. Evelyn did not particularly like Waraganj but tolerated her for her granddaughter-in-law's sake. Eleanor's enthusiasm for helping someone less fortunate was extreme, and she was chuffed to educate the poor mixed-blood young savage in white ways. She called her Mary. Florence kept to herself and was often away from the property on trips.

Waraganj – or Mary, as she became accustomed to being called – was never really sure where Florence went, and often wondered where the rest of their clan was: the children? The white women's husbands? She came to understand that the older woman's husband was dead, and would often catch her shedding a tear over the caught image of the man. Quickly wiping her eyes when Waraganj entered her room, Evelyn would say through clenched teeth, 'You fucking foolish puddenhead gin! Mary, you knock before you enter a bloody room!' Waraganj did not like going into the room anyway, where the dead man's spirit was caught in the small square fenced area and held in place by the clear material the whites called glass. The image of Evelyn Edwards' late husband sat in a wonderfully handcrafted wooden frame. His eyes followed Waraganj, and it spooked her. The old woman spooked her too. Often, she saw Evelyn staring at her from behind her knitting or needlework, or catch her at the side of the house, peering. Waraganj always thought she was doing something wrong with her chores.

Then one day a look of recognition crossed Evelyn's face, which quickly turned to disgust.

That night I found the old woman studying a family photograph that had been only taken the year before, as this 'photography' was very new. The picture featured Evelyn and her husband, Charlie, and Florence, Eleanor and Neville and another man and woman I did not know – they were not here on the property. I found out this was Bertha, the youngest daughter, together with her husband from Perth.

As I moved closer I became more intrigued by these images caught in time. I did ask Eleanor about them. There were big brick *goongees* behind the people. I could see it was a gathering of their small clan.

This matched the old man's single image caught in time. The old woman ran her finger over the face of the woman I did not know. And for a split second I looked hard and I saw me. I think? But the old woman was quick to turn sharply, gather the image to her breast and hiss, 'Get out, you heathen bitch! Get out!' I ran. Outside and to the barn. It was safer to sleep outside, for there was a look of sheer hatred in the old woman's eyes. She would surely kill me in my sleep.

On the occasions when Florence was home she managed a little conversation with Waraganj, probably hoping the gin didn't understand her much. She let her secret out that she didn't like the older woman much either, and wasn't really interested in life on the land, preferring city life instead. Waraganj's English was coming along perfectly and she understood Florence very well. She learnt that the old woman, Evelyn, was Florence's husband's mother. That Florence was bored with life on the land and missed her daughter, Bertha.

I came to understand it was Bertha in the photo, the one I saw myself in. In passing one day Florence said I had similarity in looks to her youngest. This I didn't quite understand. But it made her fonder of me, and that was nice.

There was a young white boy on the property with them; he was of simple mind, but he and Waraganj got along well. She quickly worked out that he was there to do the manual labour in the men's absence. After his chores he spent the rest of the day in the barn, carving intricate animal sculptures from bits of wood. He gave Waraganj a little wombat. Beside the kangaroo, this was the next most common animal in the area – there were wombat burrows everywhere, and if you weren't careful you could easily fall down one and break a leg. Waraganj treasured the gift.

She had been with them for nearly three months and her English was coming along fast – so much so that she could hold conversations with the women. One night, the three white women were sitting on the verandah enjoying a little supper when Waraganj came out to serve them their cups of tea, and Florence asked about her finer features and fairer skin.

Waraganj told them the story her mother had told her. Florence and Eleanor were appalled and Evelyn got up and left, mumbling profanities under her breath. Waraganj's fear of the old woman only increased. All through the birthing story Evelyn had eyeballed Waraganj, and from that day it was clear that the old woman despised her. She began calling her Black Mary. 'You might have fairer skin and finer features, gin, but always remember you are black. A nigger. A myall. A nothing. Never forget that, Mary. Black Mary.' This hurt Mary, who understood the English perfectly, but she did not let her pain show. She just nodded, indicating she understood the old woman and promised to stay out of her way.

After about eight months, the men came home from a drove and things changed quickly. When Charles Edwards returned home, Black Mary's new world came crashing down.

At first Charles didn't take much notice of the black girl who came to greet him with a quick flash of a welcoming smile and a curtsey, her head hung low in obedience and in accordance with master and servant. Florence and Eleanor excitedly filled him in on how and when the gin had shown up there, distressed and hitting her head; how they'd taught her to read and write and how she was a good hard worker, strong too.

Evelyn made her way over, but standing back and looking very stern, and made her son walk to her. Charles leant in to kiss his mother's cheek and whatever she whispered got his attention pretty quickly. He turned back hesitantly to take another look at the gin and saw immediately the resemblance in the black girl who now worked on his property. 'By God,' he muttered in disbelief. Black Mary looked similar to his younger daughter, Bertha. He froze in shock as he took her in. Evelyn's concerns were justified. She'd seen the resemblance too but hadn't mentioned it to Florence. Evelyn had wanted to keep the girl around until Charles came home, to confront him about how stupid and careless he had been to lie with a gin and have her conceive a child.

Still his wife and daughter-in-law rambled on about what a great help and company Black Mary was. His thoughts raced back to that night with the Ngarigo clan and the young girl he'd taken at gunpoint and clumsily spilt his seed into. His mother snorted her disgust and stormed off back inside, muttering, 'Trouble. Blast you all. Trouble!' He watched her go and then snapped at his wife and daughter-in-law to be silent. The chitchat could be saved for around the dinner table: for now he was weary and tired and had things to do.

Charles knew Mary could be his offspring from the gin he'd lain with on his expedition to the high country all those years ago. The young gin before him was the right age, and had a frightening resemblance to Bertha.

The next day, he ordered Black Mary away. Eleanor and Mary cried in each other's arms, which Evelyn and Charles detested. Florence was dumbfounded by her husband's harsh reaction, but he always had the final say. Mary, although she didn't know it, was berated by her own father as he personally marched her down the dirt track and out of the big gates of the property. He pushed her and she fell. Her little carved wombat that she so dearly treasured spilt from her bundle. She scampered to pick it up as her own father kicked out at her. 'Get moving, ya black bitch. And don't ever come back or I'll kill ya,' he hissed at her through clenched teeth. She left with great haste, not once looking back.

The rest of the district came to know Waraganj as Black Mary as well: 'The whitest gin around.' She became notorious for her feisty nature, sharp wit and beauty. 'An untamed filly,' the white men would say when they worked alongside her. They lusted after her. Her smarts and bravado kept her alive and stood her in good stead.

Over the years the Edwards family became rich and gave back to the area, as Charles had promised, furthering the progress and development of the old outpost. It was slow going to put the plans in motion but eventually they started taking shape. The town was to be named after the matriarch of the Edwards clan: Evelyn. By this time the area was a busy stock route and sales destination. On sale day people came from all over, so a town was much needed. It was common sense, really, but establishing the town would take time.

These days the business prowess and entrepreneurial skills of Frank Neville Charles Edwards – the only son of Eleanor and Neville, who did eventually give Charles an heir – has taken the family's fortune to even greater heights. They have made money by masterminding a lucrative business in which Frank sells local wool in Melbourne to overseas markets. This endeavour has helped keep other farmers and drovers in work and financed, but it is losing traction now because of the economic depression sweeping the world. Everyone is in trouble, including the Edwards, and that has affected the final stage of development for Everton – the preferred masculine name to Evelyn, which the town's all-male council feels is more appropriate. The locals are desperate to keep Frank in the area so he doesn't take his money elsewhere – which at one stage he and his wife, Ulla, talked about doing.

Frank has also found a wife from the city. When he was a little boy, he often went to Melbourne with his grandmother Florence on her frequent trips. So, it is no wonder he is much fonder of city living than life in the high country. He was also educated in Melbourne and received honours in his business degree. But he has kept his promise to his dying grandfather that he will get the town of Everton finished and return to the property and keep it prospering in whichever way he feels is necessary. The property has run into harder times but is doing all right considering the economic depression. The town plans for Everton have been drawn up and construction is finally underway, adding to the jailhouse, the old troopers' quarters, the Stanlow Inn, a general store and a postal house. It is exciting times as the draught horses draped in chains pull the telegraph poles into line down the newly formed street. But one of Frank's priorities is to get the new saleyards built and named before the district's next big sale day. He wants to mark the moment with fanfare, with the first of the thousands head of sheep expected to enter the gates of the Charles Edwards Saleyards.

It has been two generations since Black Mary stood on the manicured lawns of the Edwards property. Now, at either side of the garden hedge that leads to the front entrance are two mature rose bushes. The lady of the house, Mrs Ulla Edwards, nee Holznagle, is a handsome, petite woman with mousy hair – not at all the stereotypical robust German heritage qualities her name might suggest. She prunes the rose bushes, dressed immaculately, as are her children. The Edwards' high standards remain in place even though the original settlers are all long gone to their resting places.

Ulla's ten-year-old daughter, Leaellynn Florence, has sun-kissed golden curls and bright blue eyes, the Aryan race in her genes. She sits at her mother's feet and collects the dying roses, pulling off the petals and placing them in a little basket. 'They smell divine, Mama,' she says, smiling and holding a handful of plucked petals to her nose. Her porcelain doll lies on the ground beside her.

The property looks more like a hobby farm than the prosperous sheep station it once was. Empty sheds and dormant machines that once productively worked the farm lie neglected at the back of the house.

From behind the barn, eight-year-old blond, blue-eyed twin boys, Alexander Charles and Frankston Neville, come racing on wooden toy-pony sticks. Alexander Charles calls, 'Mother, I just shot me a native!'

Ulla, smiling but focused on her pruning, says, with a slight German accent, 'You say, "I just shot a native". But love all, Alexander. We are all God's creatures.'

'When will Papa be home, Mama?' Leaellynn asks.

'In a few days, darling,' Ulla replies, a smile growing on her lips.

'I miss Papa when he goes to Melbourne on business.'

'I do too. And next trip, we shall all go.'

'Promise?' The little girl smiles, beaming up at her mother.

'I promise.'

Just then an old Chinese woman comes from the house, bringing homemade lemonade. She serves it to Ulla and the children and shuffles back into the house. At the same time, an elderly Chinese man returns, lawn clippers in his hand. They are the servants on the property, prospectors who stayed in the area after the 1850s gold rush came to an end, among the many who did not make their fortune from gold.

The land is vast here. The isolated Edwards property sits on the side of a hill, with a breathtaking view out and down to the valley below. The bush is thick and the mountains in the distance roll on forever. From the trees forty yards away that line the dirt track that leads to the property, someone watches.

SEVEN

The sun's rays reach across the late-afternoon sky as if they are trying to hold on to the day. The straw of Molly's homemade broom swishes back and forth, slow but precise. Molly is unwell and lost in thought as she does the mundane chore she has done every day at this time since she arrived to live at the shanty.

Her da had her always sweep the front yard, starting at the snow gum and working back towards the front door, sweeping the dirt ground clean of the day's foot traffic. Molly asked her father why, and he answered, *It's so I know who is about, be it animal or man.*

And every morning her da would be first up, reading the land. He was a good tracker and passed this skill on to Molly. She used it well to find and hunt food for them. This gave comfort to her da that if anything happened to him, she could look after herself, for a time at least. Molly's tracking skills also came in handy when she had to find her da after he went on the drink.

Food is all gone, Molly sighs, thinking to herself.

Danny sits at the fire pit out front, staring at the small flames eating at the last of the burning coal. His siblings are playing around the back. Molly joins her son by the fire, pulling her possum-skin shawl around her. She coughs; it racks her body. Danny's rescue the day before has taken its toll. Resting her broom on the log, she takes a seat. Danny turns and smiles as his ma nestles in beside him. He thinks how grateful he is that her rescue attempt was successful. She offers him a little smile, looking down at the ground as a quick flash of yesterday's events rips through her mind. The terrifying thoughts pass and she looks to him again, she too grateful that she and her boy – no, she and her little man – have survived, and will no doubt, one day, tell the tale with smiles and bravado, the horror of the ordeal well behind.

Danny sizes up his mother's stomach, puts his little hand under her breasts. Molly sits as upright as she can and he can tell that the baby has dropped: there is space there. Molly can't help but smile. Her son is far beyond his years. She lets out a little sigh and says, 'They gotta know some time where babies come from.' Danny and Molly both smile at the prospect, knowing there will be no trip into the McGuinnesses' for the other children for this birth.

'I made some johnnycakes, Ma. Last of the flour, though.' Molly releases another sigh, deeper this time, and whispers a curse word under her breath.

'And the fish just aren't bitin'.'

She looks towards the woodheap, just an armful of broken branches left. She rubs at her temples. Danny sees her anxiety and says, 'I need to get on to fellin' that tree.' Molly knows it all too well and a look of great concern crosses her face. They are in dire conditions and winter is fast approaching. Danny feels for her and their situation. 'It might take me a day or two, or even a week but I'll get it done, Ma. I promise.'

Molly smiles again, thankful for this wonderful son, this young man with an old soul. They sit in silence a moment longer.

Maturely, Danny offers, 'Alligator's not been gone this long before.'

'He's gettin' old. Maybe . . .'

Deep down he knows that his old faithful may have wandered off to die. Molly takes up the broom to continue sweeping. With the heel of her worn and tattered shoes, she breaks down the tracks of children's feet that have hardened in the once-muddy ground, then lightly sweeps it to make a top layer of surface dirt.

'I was gonna do that, Ma.'

'It's all right, son – I need to move. Body's stiffenin' up. I'm feelin' a little better. Thank you, though.'

Danny checks the fire, only the diminishing coals remain. He heads inside and Molly follows, sweeping away his tracks. She works herself back to her front door, then looks out into the late afternoon, the shadows growing long. The old snow gum stands as the sentinel to her property, its womanly trunk prominent in the afternoon light, its outstretched branches reaching . . . *Reaching for what*, Molly would often wonder.

Molly stares hard. *Is someone there?* A cold shiver runs over her as her eyes flick to the woodheap and the dirt mound beneath it. Her eyes dart back out to her surrounds. Hitching up her skirt, she reveals a knife sheath in her sock garter and pulls from this a short-blade knife. *If anyone is out there they'll know this woman means business.* Shaking off the thought, she quickly turns, heading inside, closing and latching the door behind her.

Inside, Danny is on the floor writing, practising his letters. The others are still out the back, squabbling now. Molly is about to call them in when she is distracted by a noise coming from the front yard. It sounds like grunting and snorting. She moves slowly towards the door. Danny is lost in his writing. There it is again: grunting, snorting and . . . stomping?

Molly reaches for the latch, lifting it carefully and placing it quietly on its hook. She cracks the door open very slowly and only a hair's breadth. Her eyes widen with fright. There, standing a few feet from her front verandah, is a bloody big wild grey bullock, its horns the width of a grown man's arm span. She knows the beast could charge at the house at any time and the whole bloody thing would come crashing down without much effort at all.

'Danny,' whispers Molly. But Danny is too focused on his writing to hear his mother's concern. 'Daniel Johnson.' On hearing his full name, he brings his attention to his ma at the door. 'Gun. Now. Slow.'

He does as he is told and retrieves the gun, a Cowles & Dunn under lever single shotgun, from the utility cupboard and hands it to his mother, slow. The other children's squabbling is on the move now, coming around to the front! Still stomping and snorting, the bullock watches them rounding the corner of the shanty. On seeing the beast, they stop dead in their tracks. The bullock lowers its head as if to charge.

Molly's breath catches as the bullock jumps forward at the children. She is shaking. She cocks the shotgun but her action is clumsy and she fumbles. Danny's never seen his mother like this before.

Molly raises the gun using the doorframe as her guide, shaking and sweating profusely. Tears well in her eyes. Danny is gravely concerned not only for her but for his siblings, who are in danger of being trampled to death by this blasted beast of a bullock. Encouragingly, he whispers, 'Shoot 'im.'

Molly suddenly finds herself and pushes open the door, causing the bullock to turn and face her. Time slows around her as she steps up to the verandah post and rests her shotgun against it. The beast, lowering its head, digs at the ground with a hoof; its animal instinct is to show its authority.

Molly closes one eye and locks the other on her target, breath steady. The beast snorts, short and sharp. The children are now silent and still ... and time stops.

One single shot!

I have no control. My shotgun falls at my side and my knees buckle. I slide to the ground, the gun takin' my weight. Try as I might I could not stop this reaction even if I wanted to. I watch the bullock as it topples over. Its legs fold as it drops dead. A bullet straight between the eyes. A small trickle of blood dribbles.

The sound of the piercin' shot still ringin' out rattles me. It recoils off the range, echoing over and over in my ears. Then the screamin' of my children finally brings me out of my stupor. They race off down the back paddock. Danny stands beside me starin' down at me, dumbfounded. He's not used to seein' me like this. I never show any weakness in front of my children. Without a word he turns sharp and runs to the back door, callin' after the others, 'The bullock's dead!' With a change of tone he screams, 'The bastard's dead!'

I want to speak, say somethin', but my throat is tight, strangled with emotion. I work to find my voice but it is strained and weak. 'Rope, Danny. Rope. The snow gum. The lowest branch will do. String it up. Bleed it out. Meat. We'll have meat.'

Molly staggers to her feet and crosses to the bullock. Reaching again she takes the short-bladed knife from her sock garter. Taking one of the beast's horns, she twists its head back and bares its throat to her blade, then slices, cutting deep. Danny hogties its hind legs and the other two boys arrive to help drag it to the snow gum. By God, do they heave and heave, lifting that beast just high enough off the ground, an inch, to bleed it out, their hands red raw. Molly is fearful she might bring on the labour with all the exertion. But she cannot waste this gift. Meat. *It will not be wasted. I will not go into labour.* They will have meat for themselves and something to trade for other provisions, which are desperately needed. And the hide will make sheaths for all the children and perhaps moccasins for Danny, just in time for winter. Molly will 'waste nuttin'', just as her da taught her. 'Rely on no one. Get the job done; do it ya'self.'

Molly and her boys get to butchering the beast.

For the next week and two days, Molly and her children eat meat for breakfast, lunch and dinner. They pickle, salt, make jerky and smoke the meat using wild apple-tree wood, giving it a sweet taste. The aroma of the smokehouse is thick in the air, drawing wild dogs to the shanty. Molly chases them off with a clap of two bits of wood that sounds like a shot ringing out. 'Bloody bastard mongrel dogs!' she shouts.

Henry James stands on the verandah behind her, repeating her exact words. 'Henry James, mind ya cussin',' she tells him. The youngest of her sons goes to protest but Molly throws him a stern look. The boy knows he has overstepped the mark and slinks back inside.

That boy sure knows how to swear, she chuckles to herself. *If only he used his other words and spoke more often. Like at storytime or in their schoolin' hours or just to add to a family conversation. Maybe I should let him swear, if it'll get him talkin' proper.*

A few days pass and Molly and Danny are up on the roof, fixing the loose slats. Molly stands on a makeshift ladder handing Danny material for the repairs. He hammers with precision. It's the last days of autumn and the snow will soon be upon them. It's fallen already on the mountaintops: from up here you can see the snow-capped range stretching for miles. The site is beautiful, and Molly is lost in it as she takes a moment to appreciate her surrounds.

The other children are playing out front, Delphi under the snow gum. She loves that tree, especially when she pours water over its trunk and watches all the glorious colours magically appear, splendid hues of green, pink, purple, and even red. Joe Junior and Henry James play on the dwindling woodheap.

'Get away from there, you boys!' Danny calls from the roof.

Molly adds, 'Get around back and clean up for lunch!'

The two boys scamper off, giggling. Molly rests her eyes on the woodheap and says, 'We need to go get some more dead wood after lunch.'

'Get them rascals to drag a big branch. Tire them out a bit,' Danny says, wiping at the sweat on his brow. Molly looks at him with love, grateful for her hardworking boy. *No, young man – he turned twelve three months back.* A cold shiver runs through her. Shaking it off, her grip loosens on the ladder and she grabs a rung quickly, securing herself.

Danny breaks her thought: 'The roast is smellin' real good, Ma.'

'Bless ya, Danny. You've said that every day for near on two weeks at every roast lunch and dinner we've had. To tell ya the truth, I'm a wee bit over that blasted meat!' They both burst out laughing. Smiling, Danny offers, 'Never thought I'd ever hear ya say somethin' like that, Ma.' He goes back to his hammering as Molly takes in her surrounds again, enjoying this time with her eldest.

She's happy. Happy her children are being fed. She's a little more relaxed and there is colour in her cheeks, in all their cheeks: the meat has done them good. Even the unborn baby has benefited. It gives a little kick and Molly places her hand gently there. Now the little one rolls its heel across the top of her tummy. Molly knows that the baby has turned itself, getting ready to engage. She smiles down at her belly, silently praising the unborn child, perfect. She will soon give birth.

But her smile is short-lived and replaced with concern: in the distance coming over the hill crest she sees a covered wagon. No one uses this track unless they are lost and have stumbled across it. The wagon follows the barely visible track that leads right to her property. Molly's concern grows as she wonders who these strangers are and what do they want.

EIGHT

Wagon wheels bounce over the rocky ground of the rough track that lies beyond the thicket that hides Molly's shanty. In the back, rocking back and forth with the uncomfortable motion of the wagon as it lurches and topples over the uneven ground, Louisa Clintoff holds her sleeping son. She can barely hang on, and her face is contorted in discomfort. The wear and tear of this trip shows clearly in her tired and worn eyes. She coughs and sniffles – perhaps she is coming down with something? The inside of the covered wagon shows signs of floodwater. Some of their belongings, including her clothes, have been waterlogged, and there are traces of mud.

'Nate?' she calls, not too loudly, not wanting to wake the little boy. 'Nate, please?' She has had enough. Coughing racks her body.

The covered wagon comes to a stop, and her handsome husband, Sergeant Nate Clintoff, swings down from the front bench seat; he too is looking more than a little worn out by the epic journey from Melbourne to Everton. He stretches, rubbing at his thigh, the one ripped apart by enemy fire in the war, then walks the length of the wagon, noting the water marks on the cover and mud and debris still caught in the wheel spokes. He traces his hand along the wagon as he recalls the ordeal.

A few weeks back now, the Clintoffs ran into trouble. Nate, not being a man of the land, misjudged the pull of the current of a swollen river. The horses couldn't manage the rushing water and the weight of the wagon, and they all got swept away. Nate and Louisa were lucky to come out of it with their own lives, let alone the lives of their horses and the majority of their possessions.

I take the gamble and keep the horses attached to the wagon for as long as I can. They fight and struggle to keep their heads above the water. I pray that the wagon or the horses will find a sandbank, or the wagon gets snagged on a branch. Eventually a wheel hits something, bringing it a sudden halt. I jump into the raging water, holding on to the wagon. I work my way to the back, then lift the flap and pull myself in. Louisa starts crying with relief on seeing me. She sits in water up to her waist, everything we own floating around her. She clings to Samuel, who is too afraid to do anything but hang on to his mother for dear life.

We embrace and I take them in my arms, kissing their brows, trying to soothe them, though doubting every action I have taken in my rescue attempt. Louisa's eyes widen with fear when I tell her my plan, but I reassure her it is for the best. And I do my best to believe it.

I take Samuel as Louisa rips fabric from her petticoats and drapes it as a sling around our son, who is sitting high on my back. She knots it off as tightly and securely as she can and then strips down to her undergarments, as I instructed, so the weight of the wet fabric of her dress and petticoats won't drag her under. We then plunge into the cold raging river. Just as I'd hoped, the current forces us up against the wagon cover. We make our way to the front carefully, where the horses are just managing to keep their heads above water. I'm clear in my instructions to my beautiful wife: hang on to the mane of one of the horses as tightly as you can and don't let go. The look of horror in her eyes breaks my heart. 'Trust me,' I say, choked with emotion. She only manages a nod. 'The horse will find ground eventually. Let him have his head, hang on and float. Go with the current.' I kiss her deeply. 'I love you. I will find you, I promise. You will be fine.'

Louisa takes the long, strong strands of wet horsehair in her small, delicate hands and with that, I reach under the water to pull the leather straps off the harness and the first horse drifts away with the pull of the floodwater. Louisa, hanging on for dear life, looks back at me and Samuel, no doubt wondering if this will be the last time she sees us. Angst and distress fill her eyes. The brave girl smiles, knowing if it is to be our last time she does not want me haunted by the fear in her face.

I pause briefly to watch her turn back to face the raging river and the danger we both must confront – and survive! For our son, for each other. Our new adventure has just got overwhelmingly serious and very real. For a split second I think of home: Louisa's garden, of all things! My family, friends and dear England. I watch Louisa tighten her grip on the horse's blessed mane to position herself higher in the water, ready to face whatever Mother Nature has to give. Not wanting her to get too far ahead, I quickly release the second and third horses. Then, holding firm to the fourth, our son strapped to my back, I cut the leather strap and release the animal from the constraints of the wagon. It washes away with the force of the murky brown floodwater.

A small cry from inside the wagon brings Nate out of his memory and he shakes it off, limps to the back and opens the flap. Samuel springs eagerly into his father's open arms. With his free hand, he helps his wife out of the wagon. Louisa rubs at her bottom, coughing again.

'Lord have mercy upon my aching bones.' She hugs at herself; a fever coming on, perhaps?

They share a smile for the first time in days, happy to be alive and on dry ground. Louisa sees the shanty and says, 'You've found help.' She kisses her husband, thanking him. She and Nate both take a deep breath, smelling Molly's roast lunch. Arm in arm, they head towards the shanty.

Molly stands watching and waiting on her verandah, her faithful Cowles & Dunn shotgun by her side. Her children are inside, peering through the gaps in the wooden slat walls. They are not accustomed to visitors, who more often than not are not friend but foe. Molly and her little family keep to themselves and mind their own business. She has been like this all her life; her da was the same. 'No one's business but ours,' he would often say. 'We are all the family we need.' The wagon that has arrived in her front yard is not welcomed or wanted. Not now, anyway: *I only have two bullets left.*

The Clintoffs weave their way through the thicket and Molly sizes them up as they approach. *They're city folk: they don't carry guns. They look to be trustworthy. Travel weary. A woman present is always a good sign. Petite. Pretty.* She notices the man's limp: *He's injured – even better.*

They are near the woodheap when Nate calls out hello. Molly brings her gun up. 'State ya business.'

A little taken-aback, the Clintoffs stop in their tracks, not wanting to offend the woman with the gun or put themselves in further danger. 'Sergeant Nate Clintoff. My wife, Louisa, and our son, Samuel. Heading to Everton. Couldn't help but smell your roast ...'

Nate is a little embarrassed by what he has just said, but he's hungry, and they haven't eaten in days. All their food provisions were lost to the floodwater.

Molly is taken aback by his audacity.

Louisa looks at Nate, appalled. Scoffing at his remarks, she asks the woman with the gun to forgive her husband and proceeds to explain their dilemma. 'We've been travelling for some time now, Missus ...?'

'Johnson. Missus Joe Johnson,' Molly informs them, curtly.

'Up from Melbourne – well, out from London actually, Missus Johnson. It's been a long nine-and-a-half weeks of travel.

Nate chimes in, 'Crossing the river further south we had some trouble and lost all our provisions.'

A quick glance at the wagon again and Molly notes the waterline: *The floodwater – they're not lyin'.*

Louisa continues, 'And well, the smell of your cooking, the aroma travelled. We feel terrible in asking—'

Nate interrupts: 'We can see you don't have much—'

'We make do, thank you,' Molly responds, defensively.

Louisa blushes, embarrassed for her husband. She fans her face and says as an aside, 'Nate Clintoff, you are not helping.' Calling again to the woman with the gun, she says, 'If we could join you for your meal? We'll share one plate between us; we won't intrude at your table.'

Nate starts to look around him, sniffing at the air, looking for the odour. Molly becomes aware of his suspicion. Samuel wriggles restlessly in his father's arms, distracting him from his investigation. Molly notices the gentleness of the man as he places his son down, and the poise of the woman; trusting people? She looks back at the covered wagon and gets an idea.

Louisa makes a final attempt to win Molly over. 'We would be forever indebted to you,' she implores, with an awkward smile.

Molly plays along, drawing out the moment. She's no pushover, and she'll hold her ground to anyone. She calculates her thought, then says, finally, 'To Everton, ya say?' Nate and Louisa nod.

Samuel has made his way to the verandah and pokes a finger into a hole and with the other hand slips his little fat fingers through a gap in the slats. Giggling is heard from inside. Samuel turns back to his parents with a big grin on his face. He pokes and prods again, and this time the giggles become laughter and Molly's four children race from inside. Samuel is as thrilled to see the children as Louisa is. They run, swirling around her with Samuel in tow. Louisa turns to Molly, exclaiming, 'Oh my, how blessed you are.'

No argument or denyin' that – especially when it comes to my precious children. Molly proudly squares her shoulders, smiling for the first time in their presence, and motions the Clintoffs inside.

NINE

Black sallee trees line the dirt track to the Edwards property; all is still and quiet but for the caws of crows. A gentle breeze soothes the trees. The serenity is broken by the gallop of horses' hooves. Frank Edwards has returned home from Melbourne, his small travel provisions tied to his saddle.

Around forty-five years old, of slight build, he wears a pinstripe business suit and his much-loved Staker hat. He doesn't look like your typical farmer. He is a forward thinker, an entrepreneur who has orchestrated the sale of local wool overseas, bringing the money back to the community.

As he approaches, Frank looks eagerly for his children. His forehead creases with concern: they would normally be running down the track to greet him with big smiles and squeals of delight, pushing each other for prime position to get to their father first. His smile falls away as he takes in the house. It is deathly quiet. But then he looks to the lawn out front: and there his family are, wife and three children, sitting under a tree. It appears they are having a picnic, but there is no movement.

At first, he thinks it's a game. He calls to them: 'Ulla! Leaellynn! Alexander? Frankston?' But there's no answer, and as he gets closer the smell hits him. Hard. His smile is instantly replaced with a grim frown of horror, just as his wife topples over from where she sits.

He swings down from his horse, his feet meeting the ground

at pace and already in stride as he races towards them. There before him are his wife and children, lifeless. Murdered. His family have been propped up around the base of a tree, rose petals sprinkled around them. Sprawled on the ground close by is the little basket that Leaellynn collected the petals in. The corpses look as though they have been there at least a week, but the crisp mountain air has kept decomposition to a minimum.

Frank drops to his knees, sobbing. His broken-hearted, sorrowful cries echo around the range and turn to yells of frustration, anguish and pain. He runs to his horse and races off to town for help.

In this part of the country the mountain range runs in all directions, a worn track dividing them down the middle. Behind a cluster of young snow gums, someone is crouching. Before him lies the track, the main thoroughfare to Everton – a wooden sign indicates this. The town Sergeant Nate Clintoff will soon be running, still very much ruled by mountain law and mountain ways.

There is movement behind the cluster of snow gums; tentatively, an Aboriginal man, forty years old, handsome, strong and athletic – although severely injured by a stab wound to his lower back – stumbles, exhausted, from the trees. His breathing is shallow: he's been running and his face is etched with anxiety and guilt as he looks around, taking in his surrounds. He shifts the iron collar that sits around his neck, revealing deep cuts to his collarbone where it has been rubbing. The iron collar indicates only one thing: that at some stage this man has been in custody. He wipes at the sweat on his brow, dried blood on his hands and on his torn and dirty calico pants and shirt – clothing that is officially distributed to felons. Embroidered on the chest pocket are the words 'Government property'.

Yadaka staggers onto the track. He can't believe he has made it this far. He has been running for days, with no time to stop and eat, carrying a wound that has become dangerously infected. He only has to clear the southern range and get onto the Great Dividing and head north, homeward bound, to Guugu Yimithirr country, his mother's country, land of rainforest and coloured sands. It is a walk that will take him months, but a walk he is willing to make to get back to country: a place now called Queensland by the whites. Other than meeting his adopted family and finding his life partner and having children, prior to this his life has been extremely traumatic.

Yadaka's breath catches as a sharp pain rips through his back, so powerful that his head spins. He feels sick to his stomach, the pain made worse by having not eaten in days. Before he can come to his senses and steady himself, Frank Edwards is upon him, his horse rearing to a halt. The black man freezes.

The horse rears again, spooked. Frank tries to bring the animal under control. At the same time, he takes in the appearance of the man before him: *Black. The collar. Bloodstained clothes.* He reaches for his pistol, saying, 'Murderer! You killed them! You killed my wife and children!'

Yadaka grabs a handful of debris from the track and throws it in Frank's face, momentarily blinding him, and races back into the cluster of young snow gums, falling in the long grass. He lies in great pain, too exhausted to fight if Frank chooses to hunt him. Yadaka slowly lifts himself to see, peering through the stalks of tussock grass, watching, waiting.

Dismounting, Frank brushes the dirt from his face and heads in the direction the black man went. Tentatively, he treads lightly, afraid – he's a man who does not favour any sort of confrontation. From behind him, a crow takes flight. He turns quickly, bringing his pistol up to shoot, but stops on seeing the black bird. In a frenzy he looks around, becoming disoriented. It's too much for him, and he backs away to his horse, calling again, 'You killed my family! You'll hang for this, you dirty heathen savage!' And with that, he mounts his horse and races towards Everton.

Yadaka is relieved and closes his eyes. This is too much. Maybe he would be better off dead? What kind of future does he have in a land where he and his people are treated like a stubborn stain on a white linen shirt? Like shit on the sole of a shoe? A race of people living with targets on their heads, all because of their difference. Hunted, massacred, eradicated, dispersed – foreign words associated with being black in this land now. He has lived through all the attempts, putting his own body on the line for himself and his loved ones. These words are evident in the diaries of people he has worked for and journals of the superiors who have arrested him. Leaving their books open, not realising or thinking that a black man has the brain capacity to know how to read. The dramas, the facades. There has been no peace in his life for a very, very long time.

Yadaka sighs. It sounds like his last breath, perhaps: the pain, the heartache, the constant worry and fear of what the next day will bring. It's all becoming too much, knowing your next breath could be your last just because of the colour of your skin.

Yadaka, a man known for his fighting skill, his courage and strength, his sensibility and his smile, rolls over to alleviate the ache in his back. He grabs at it, revealing in his hand blood and a yellow substance indicating a nasty infection. With the weight of the world on his shoulders, he finally closes his eyes and releases the tears that have pooled there. He whispers to death, 'Take me.'

He hears the caw of the crow overhead. It calls again, this time flying low directly over Yadaka and perching in the branches above him. It cries out again. Is this the message of death? It caws again, and this time there is an urgency in the bird's call. Yadaka's eyes open slowly and he finds focus on the bird. It tilts its head and its eye finds his. 'Yes, Grandmother, I'm coming.'

Yadaka springs up and races off, putting distance and time between him and this encounter. He must keep moving, or he will die.

TEN

The embers in Molly's stove burn low. She, her children and the Clintoffs sit around the table, eating quietly. Everyone has a plate of meat and freshly found and roasted yams. Molly focuses on her food, avoiding conversation with the strangers, doubting her invitation for them to join her and her children for lunch: *What was I thinkin'?*

Louisa delicately takes a small mouthful of food from her fork as she watches Molly's children – the little girl beautiful, the three boys handsome, and all of them very well mannered. She looks to Molly, a tinge envious. Louisa can only hope that one day she will have more children and they will be as well behaved as these precious ones. That was one of the stipulations of coming all the way to Australia: Nate promised they would give Samuel siblings.

Molly senses Louisa watching her and turns to face her. Louisa offers a gentle smile as she swallows her food. 'So delicious and gracious of you, really ... thank you.'

Molly smiles shyly, her confidence dissolved in the face of these strangers. After a moment, she gives a sideways glance to Louisa and watches her eat, her poise, her decorum, so ladylike. Her hair soft and shiny, her skin clear and smooth, even though it is very evident that they have travelled far and maintenance of the lady's appearance hasn't been a priority. Resigned, Molly goes back to her eating. She knows she doesn't have a ladylike bone in her body or the lifestyle to be as cared for and kept as Louisa Clintoff.

They all eat in silence. Nate reaches for another piece of the roast, and as he goes to stab it with his fork he springs out of his chair, rubbing his hand frantically up and down his thigh. He gives his leg a shake. Everyone turns to watch him, the children and Molly jumping with fright.

'Sorry, didn't mean to scare you all,' says Nate, wincing slightly. 'Injury plays up now and then. Got to stretch it out.'

Danny is intrigued and pipes up: 'Ya da do that to ya, mister?'

Nate is taken aback by Danny's comment. He and Louisa exchange glances.

'Danny! Mind ya business,' Molly chides. She busies herself with moving food around her plate.

Louisa and Nate register Molly's awkwardness, and Nate offers up his story to ease the embarrassment. 'No – in the line of duty.'

Danny, grateful for the conversation, asks if he is a soldier. 'Was,' says Nate. He continues to rub his thigh, hoping to alleviate the pain.

Louisa chimes in: 'Sergeant Clintoff was a great solider, injured whilst rescuing a fellow comrade. Still wanting to work for his country in the armed forces, he took up desk duties and worked at headquarters for many years, doing very well.' She looks across at her husband, smiling reassuringly even though it was that very job that destroyed his soul and sank him into his depression. 'And now here we are on a new adventure. To run a town in the bush! In Australia! That's why we're here.'

Danny, very impressed, says, 'The boss of Everton?'

Nate looks at him, smiling proudly. 'I'm here to uphold the law and apply new legislation.'

Molly moves uncomfortably in her chair.

'I'd like to become the boss of Everton one day. When I'm bigger,' Danny says.

Nate can't help but smile at the boy's enthusiasm. 'That's a fine idea – maybe you will. You can come and work for me. I'll show you the ropes.'

'Think I might go to London someday too.' Danny is about to say more, but his mother cuts him off.

Molly informs Nate that he's just in time for the sales. Nate agrees, saying he was supposed to be here a few days earlier to settle in, but due to being caught up in the floods a few days back, their arrival has been delayed. 'About a week back now,' he says.

Danny is happy to add to the conversation: 'That's about right, mister, if ya comin' from the south. I got caught in the fresh too. Ma saved me. See, Delphi dropped her dolly in the water—'

'Enough,' Molly chides him again.

'No. The water took my dolly!' Delphi interjects.

Nate offers Danny a sympathetic smile, saying, 'The fresh can sure catch up on you.'

Danny isn't game to speak but gives Nate a tight-lipped smile and a nod in agreement.

An awkward silence follows, and Molly feels it. If she doesn't make conversation, God knows what her son will say next. She offers up that the town comes to life when the sales are on. 'People come from all over. And the sheep will be down from the high country soon. That's where my husband is – he's a drover.'

Nate and Louisa both listen to this with great interest. Nate takes in his surroundings, the run-down state of the place. Molly sees this and is quick to say, 'He's been away three months.'

Louisa happily adds, 'Nate and I haven't been away from each other's side since we were married.' She has missed the underlying tension in Molly's statement, but Nate hasn't. He turns to his wife, who is gazing lovingly at him. She looks to Molly, eager for a love story to compare.

Molly offers a lame little smile as she tries to hide her discomfort. *What the hell do I know about affection?* she thinks. *A husband's love? Companionship?* These are foreign concepts in Molly and Joe's relationship. He's hardly home, and that's just how Molly likes it. Molly considers Louisa's loving gaze towards her husband – she's never seen that look in a woman's eyes before. *That must be what love looks like.* Molly takes a moment to mimic the *look of love*, hoping to add some sincerity to her story.

'Love watchin' my Joe canterin', across the flats, comin' home, sun settin' behind him. The children runnin' to greet him. Wavin' his hat with joy on seein' 'em ...'

Molly gazes at her children, who are mesmerised by what she's just said. There is a tinge of disbelief in their looks to their ma. She smiles at them with love and encourages them: 'Eat up.'

Louisa watches Molly closely. She has noticed the change in her persona. A little perplexed but not sure on what grounds to base this judgement, she lets the thought go. Molly turns to her, offering a big smile. 'Ya's should be on ya way if you intend to get to Everton by nightfall.'

Molly rises to take their plates. Louisa jumps up to help, but Molly shifts the plates out of her reach. Louisa is taken aback by the abruptness of Molly's action. Molly feels this and offers her a comforting and reassuring smile. 'Please, you're my guest.'

Molly steps away to the wash bucket. Her children quickly shovel the remainder of their food into their mouths. Finishing, they get up and take their plates, clearing the table. Louisa takes in the children's well-worked routine, impressed. Molly starts washing up and each child grabs a rag to wipe the plates and utensils. Danny clears Nate's and Samuel's plates. As quickly as the cleaning-up starts it is all over, with everyone chipping in to help.

Louisa straightens out her skirt and takes a washcloth Delphi offers up. Samuel has thoroughly enjoyed his lunch and has gravy all over his little face. Louisa turns to Molly: 'Thank you again, Missus Johnson. Lovely to meet you and your beautiful well-mannered children.' She turns to Nate. 'We need to attend to the horses and get going.'

Nate rises, lifting Samuel with him. 'Spoken like a true bush woman. Her first time out of the big smoke.' He smiles at his wife. Molly sees this and watches Louisa a little enviously. Samuel kisses his father on the chin and Nate responds by blowing a raspberry on his son's chubby cheek. Samuel giggles with delight.

Danny smiles, a boy in awe of this father–son relationship. Nate sees Danny watching and playfully ruffles his hair. They smile at each other. They like each other.

Louisa enthusiastically chimes in, 'I'm looking forward to the challenges of life on the land.'

Molly comes to stand by the table. 'I wish you all the very best with that then, Missus Clintoff.' Her ironic tone is present and deliberate and Louisa knows it. She feels a little foolish about what she's said, though she meant every word. Louisa desperately wants to strike a connection with Molly – she likes her. 'If ever you're in town, perhaps we can meet?'

'My Joe brings the supplies home, and town's a fair distance.'

Louisa frowns. 'Oh dear! Really? I was hoping we were nearly there.'

Nate has started to move off towards the front door. Samuel waves goodbye to the other children and they wave back. Louisa follows but then stops, turns back and wishes Molly the very best with her birth. 'Looks like any day now.'

Molly smiles shyly, caught out by Louisa's sincerity. Female company and talk about women's stuff is new to Molly. If it were another time, perhaps she would try harder to befriend Louisa, but right now she just can't.

Louisa is almost out the door. 'We truly are indebted to you.'

Molly drops her thoughts about a possible friendship and, not missing a beat, quickly responds, 'Good. I've a favour to ask.'

Molly can't believe her luck: a ride to Everton for her children! Finally, something is going her way – although, in saying that, luck has been falling her way of late and she hopes it continues.

As the two women walk towards the wagon, Louisa talks like a giddy young girl. 'I hope to start a women's group as well. My mama started one of the first women's movements in Britain.'

Molly can't help but smile at Louisa's enthusiasm. Louisa sees this and feels a little foolish. The woman who walks beside her has clearly had a hard life and doesn't have much. Louisa's cheeks blush a powdered rose. 'Oh, look at me. Talking like an excited naive little girl. I'm sorry – I haven't spoken to another woman for nearly two weeks now.' Molly bites her tongue with her reality. 'Thank you again for the meal, Missus Johnson.'

They reach the covered wagon that sits out the front of Molly's shanty. All the children are in the back, giggling with excitement. They each hold a small parcel of clothes and food for the journey. Meat for trading is piled in beside them. Molly offered some to the Clintoffs for their trouble. They refused at first but Molly insisted – she doesn't want the meat going off. She motions to her three youngest and they come to her for kisses, cuddles and final grooming with spit-on-thumb as she clears the gravy caught at the corner of Joe Junior's mouth. Delphi clings to her mother for an extra-long moment; no spit is required – Delphi is immaculate.

This is Delphi's first time away from her ma and she's a little upset, but excited by the adventure that awaits her. She has often heard from her brothers how wonderful Miss Shirley's sweets and cakes are, and the excitement of coming home to a little baby sister or brother far outweighs her fear and sadness at leaving.

'I love ya's. Ya hear me? I love ya's! Mind ya manners at the McGuinnesses'.'

She spits on her fingertips to tame that one blasted strand of Henry James's hair that just won't sit down. Then a ritual: a clenched fist to their foreheads, a breath released through the fist and the whispered words, 'Always with you.' Nate and Louisa watch on, puzzled.

The children quietly find their places in the back of the wagon. Molly motions Danny to her. Nate places a small barrel of water in the wagon as Molly talks to Danny in a soft but stern tone: 'Make sure ya brothers and sister behave, now. Get a good trade with the meat. Fresh veggies, the greener the better. Donkey or horse, either will do, but no nag. And don't forget the other supplies. Bullets are low.' She places a piece of paper, a list, in his shirt pocket.

Sergeant Clintoff has seen and heard all of this. He looks to Molly, a little perplexed, and thinks to himself for a second, remembering that he heard her say her husband was bringing home the supplies, but he doesn't say anything or think much of it. He's grateful for the meal, and what Molly asks of her son is her business. He heads to the front of the wagon, shaking out his leg as he goes.

Molly steps back, smiling. 'Get some of Miss Shirley's cakes and sweets into ya skinny-malinky long legs.' Just as her da would whisper to her on the rare occasions he left her with Miss Shirley when he went a drovin', hoping the sweets would soften the blow of being left behind. 'But then straight home, son. I'll need help.'

Molly rubs at her very pregnant belly with a warming smile. Danny nods. He looks a little scared at the prospect – this will be his first delivery. When Delphi was born, he took himself and his younger brothers to stay with the McGuinnesses and brought them home the following week all safe and sound to see their little sister.

Danny remembers the words his mother said to him a few months back: 'I'm getting on, Danny. My age might be a problem for me now, so I need ya with me at the birth.' Danny had turned pale and Molly had a chuckle to herself. 'Eventually, son, ya gotta know where babies come from.'

The covered wagon pulls away and the children wave and shout their goodbyes. From up front, Louisa looks back and gives Molly a gracious smile and a little wave. Molly offers a nod of appreciation. Then, as if it's a second thought, she calls out more instructions: 'No fightin'. Ya hear me, Joe Junior? Henry James? I love ya's!'

Her emotions run high as she watches the wagon trundle down the track. Then she sighs with relief. Big relief. Molly needs this time to herself before the baby comes, but there is more to this moment, more to the release this moment brings. This alone time will do her well in more ways than one.

The wagon with her little family disappears down the barely visible track. Her family: her life. Without her children Molly Johnson doesn't know where she would be. Her children are her world, and she would do anything for them. She continues to watch as the wagon becomes a speck on the horizon. Before them the broad mountain range looms, snow caps on its highest peaks.

*

The shadows of the mountains creep across the open plains of the alpine country. Danny looks back to where they have come from. He can't help but be concerned for his ma. His brothers and sister talk excitedly to Louisa, who has joined them in the back, and he smiles at their enthusiasm. A stranger, someone new to talk to. Louisa tells them about the journey out from London on the big ship to Melbourne. The younger children are enthralled, and secretly so is Danny. He looks back in the direction of his home, but nothing can be seen of their property from here.

The wagon wheels bounce over the rocks, disturbing a herd of brumbies grazing nearby. The stallion of the herd stands on guard. Danny turns to where the brumby looks and in the distance, dust stirs on the horizon.

ELEVEN

Three stockmen amble along on their horses, moving a few thousand head of sheep. The head stockman, Robert Parsen, has fiery-red hair and a full beard and is built like a bullock. Tied to his horse is a mare that looks a little spooked and unkempt, unusual for a stockhorse – a stockman's horse is his prized possession.

Parsen clutches in his coat front a baby lamb that couldn't walk the distance. 'Not sure what I'm gonna do with you, little one,' he says gently, peering down at the lamb, which sleeps soundly.

Another voice, as if almost reading Parsen's mind, comes from behind: it's John McPharlen, the youngest of the stockmen. There is a deviant quality to him. His eyes appear too narrow and too close together for him to be trustworthy. 'Ya gonna hafta take care of it now. The mother won't want nuttin' to do with it, smellin' ya all over it, ya big bastard.' He laughs, cantering off to the outside of the herd. But Parsen will take the chance and try to reintroduce the lamb once they get to the saleyard, or make it his mission to find it a home; otherwise it'll be lamb's fry. The latter is more likely.

Robert Parsen comes from English convict stock. His great-grandfather came to Australia on the First Fleet, convicted of murder, and was granted his freedom after rescuing a captain from an attack by local blacks. Parsen's great-grandfather was a hard man – killed the three blacks with his bare hands. He could fight like a thrashing machine and Parsen has inherited this trait. His great-grandfather acquired land for his efforts and became a farmer. Parsen's father was born on the property, as were Robert and his two brothers.

In 1847, the family moved to the newly founded town of Maryborough in Queensland with other colonial entrepreneurs to establish a pastoral station. Maryborough was to become a major port for Queensland's south-east, and Parsen's father saw future opportunities for himself and his sons. It was in those parts that Parsen first witnessed the true hardship and brutality of the Australian way of life. There was a brutal attack on the local Ginginbarra clan. Twenty-eight squatters were killed in the bloodbath, Parsen's mother being one of the casualties.

Two years later, thirteen-year-old Robert took revenge, together with 21-year-old Gregory Blaxland, the seventh son of an adventurous explorer of the time. He and Robert headed a vigilante posse of some fifty squatters and station hands who, at Bingera, ambushed a group of a hundred sleeping myalls of the Gin Gin tribe.

'We'll wait till after one of their big dance-ups. They sleep sounder and wake later after one of those nights.'

'How do ya know?' a weary voice called from the back of the group.

'I've slept out. And seen it with my own eyes,' a confident young Robert Parsen replied.

Having learnt early how to handle a gun, Parsen was quite the marksman in spite of his young age. He picked off many of the blacks, even those diving into the Burnett River to flee. The slaughter was violent and undiscriminating. It forever embedded a ruthlessness in Parsen and cemented his attitude towards the blacks beyond repair.

Parsen continues to maintain a vendetta towards the blacks for killing his mother, even though it was a bullet that finished her. She was caught in the crossfire, killed by one of their own.

'Well, if it wasn't for the blacks killin' in the first place this wouldn't have happened!' young Robert cried. And that was the last time he ever shed a tear for anyone.

His father was already a tough, hard-drinking man, but after his wife's death he became violently cruel towards his sons. The three boys were forced to leave home early to find their way in the world, Robert only fourteen. They went their separate ways and lost track of each other.

Robert Parsen turned to droving, which takes him up and down the east side of the country, and occasionally up into the Northern Territory, traversing thousands of miles of rough terrain moving livestock along the stock routes. His only possessions are his horse, his hat and his boots. When he isn't droving and living under the stars, he ventures to the larger towns and lives at a brothel or a hotel until his next drove. He never has to wait very long.

Parsen, tough and stoic, has a life that consists of livestock, his fellow drovers and his good mates John McPharlen and Joe Johnson, with whom he rides for months at a time. He befriended Johnson a little over ten years ago, and together they favour the high-country droves in the alpine country, drawn to the isolation, harshness and beauty of the land. They are skilled drovers: loss or death of livestock under their watch is extremely rare, and their ability to push their herd to get the best grazing ground and be first to market to get the best prices is legendary, spoken about around camp fires. Their mateship was cemented firm and fast when they saved each other's lives in an all-in brawl, but the two men share a similar past: both lost their mother at a young age and were left with a cruel father who took his grief out on his son.

Parsen has never married and is not interested in giving up the freedom of the droving life. Johnson is married, but keeps his family life away from his work life. Parsen has never officially met Joe's wife, Molly, but respects her from afar. He tips his hat to her when she and the children follow Joe out as he sets off on the drove. Molly always lingers behind – she only follows for the children's sake. She's not in the marriage for love, but for convenience, status and children – that much is clear to Parsen, and Johnson has told him so.

High on a rocky outcrop, whisky bottle almost empty, Robert Parsen and Joe Johnson would talk.

'Puttin' up with married life?' Parsen would ask.

'Well, it's simple,' Johnson would say. 'I make sure I have plenty of work that keeps me away. I bed her when I get home to keep the children comin', which she wants, and she ain't that bad on the eye. And my clothes are washed and folded and meals prepared and then I'm gone again. Simple, see?' And they would both roar with laughter.

Prior to the founding of Everton, Robert Parsens' world was independent and lawless. He and his younger sidekick John McPharlen were a law unto themselves. They don't respect anything or anyone and their hearts and souls have grown hard, like the high country they so love. With townships springing up everywhere and new laws being enforced, their reign of loud-mouthed drunken terror is under threat. They plan to make the most of hitting town the following night. Word is out that the new peace keeper and upholder of Her Majesty's law has finally arrived in Everton.

McPharlen breaks the monotony of the drove with a whistle to the dogs. A few sheep have swung too wide and the dogs give chase. McPharlen indicates to his boss through hand signals what has happened and Parsen nods his approval. McPharlen smiles back, baring his rotten teeth, then whistles again to the dogs as they nip at the heels of the sheep, turning them back into the flock.

The story of their meeting is an interesting one.

McPharlen's mother was a foul-mouthed whore with no morals and not a single tooth. People called her crazy. She took all her frustrations out on little John, who would just fall to the ground, roll himself up as tight as he could and let her beat him. She rarely fed him and he never bathed. He stank. He wasn't 'gone in the head' as the local people thought – just neglected and introverted.

When McPharlen was ten years old, Parsen was fucking McPharlen's mother when the presence of the boy standing at the side of the bed caught his attention. He was about to climax when he looked up and saw the naked boy, who said, 'Wanna fin-fin-finish on mmm-mmee for a-a-a p-p-p-enny?'

Parsen rolled off and away from the woman and the boy as little John climbed on the bed, offering himself. Parsen swore at them both, calling the mother 'a sick bitch to sell her helpless son'. The woman turned on the boy, beating him. Parsen wasn't known to be a soft man at all, but there was something about this boy, and whatever it was, it got to him. He backhanded the woman away from the young McPharlen, sending her sprawling across the room. He gathered the clothes he could find of the boy's, throwing them at him and ordering him to put them on, and to never do that again. And then Parsen took him with him everywhere.

They have been together ever since. The boy has grown into a better person, as best as Parsen could manage: he's stopped stuttering and bathes more often, and his nightmares are long gone. He looks up to Parsen and would do anything for him.

The dogs nip at the heels of the sheep at the back, they pick up pace, creating a ripple across the flock. The stockmen hope optimistically to make town by nightfall. The setting sun sends a golden glow across the plains, silhouetting the men and their livestock. As it darkens, the sky is blanketed with a brilliant spray of stars.

TWELVE

Next morning, dew sparkles on leaves in the early morning light. Steam rises off the hot spring hidden in the thicket, a little alcove protecting this beautiful spot. Another gift from Mother Earth. A person has to get lost to find it.

Molly lies half-submerged in the steaming water, her pregnant belly on display in all its maternal glory. Beautiful and calm, she floats, not a care in the world – no weight on her shoulders today. Her mind is free of thought or concern, calmed by the tranquil sounds of nature. She's just in the moment, in the here and now.

Gently, she lifts and lowers her hand up and out of the water, playing with the run-off at her fingertips. She repeats this a few times then, as if bored from the rest, slowly submerges herself fully under the water; bubbles come from her nose as she pushes her untied hair back from her face.

Molly rises out of the water like Mother Nature herself, refreshed, energised and ripe for birth. Today will be the day. Treading lightly and carefully, she heads for the bank, gathers her ochre-red shift dress and slips it over her wet, naked body, blooming with life. The freshness of the air bites at her wet skin, and Molly enjoys the crispness.

She heads off, collecting her shotgun from where it leans against a tree. She looks beautiful in the morning light, her wet light-brown hair cascading down past her shoulders, longer than one would expect. She usually wears it in a loose bun, a rogue ringlet or two shaping her face and giving her a soft edge, but today it falls freely. The ochre-red of her dress contrasts against the green of the ferns and the silver of the white sallees, and floats around her. She looks relaxed for the first time in a long while.

I look up at the hill that will deliver me home, keen to tackle it. Challenge accepted. The walk, the hill climb and my bath in the springs will help bring on my labour, hopefully today. What joy this new life will bring to me and the children! A birth is always a gift, and precious. I was an only child myself, so always wanted many children of my own – it's why I agreed to marry Joe. Secretly I hope it's a little girl – a sister and playmate for my Delphi.

I know what it's like to grow up without a mother. I know what it's like to live without a mother's love – without her touch, her kiss, her voice, her smell. I want to give my children what I never had, shower them with so much love and affection that they never forget me. If anythin' ever happens to me, they will know they were loved and I will be remembered.

To not know your ma is a pain that is indescribable. Actually, pain is not the right word – the feelin' is an emptiness, a hole in your soul. It's deep, really deep. Somethin' missin' … just not complete … There is no access to it, no path walked, no direction given, because she, my ma, was never there. My da and I, we never spoke of *her*. Only sometimes when he was drunk he'd blurt inaudible, nonsensical sentences and break into song: 'Black is the colour of my true love's hair.' He had his pain, too. Because he knew *her*.

But me? As a little girl I would dream of a woman with long flowin' black hair ...

With the serene sounds of nature guiding her way, Molly steps high to clear fallen logs, through clusters of sweetgrass, and comes to a small cleared area, Mother Nature's doing. She runs her hand through the tall sweetgrass spikelets. A few male flame robins flitter from stalk to stalk, red chests against the frost-burn browning of the sweetgrass – a sign winter is coming. The robin's pretty birdsong is interrupted by a crow's caws in the distance.

A dragonfly hovers, its magnificent metallic colours shimmering in the morning light. It begins to move – up then down, back then forward, then away. The dragonfly to some is considered a symbol of strength, courage and happiness, like Molly this morning. But in other folklore the dragonfly is deemed to be sinister. Another dragonfly hovers over a spikelet, then up then down, back then forward, then away.

Soon Molly reaches the edge of the clearing and moves deeper into the dense green of the thicket at the base of the hill. She grows smaller but her rusty-red dress defines her against the bush as she nears the base of her climb home. She pauses as she sizes it up. Hands on hips, a deep breath, she starts the incline.

From behind, at the edge of the clearing, there's a sound of breaking twigs. A shadowed hand rests on a tree trunk. Someone is following her.

'Don't you move!' echoes around the range.

Molly cocks her shotgun with great force and takes aim. She has reached the plateau where her shanty sits, but before her, face down on the ground, is a badly injured Aboriginal man. Molly can see the wound on his back clearly through his tattered shirt. She recoils at the stench of both the injury and the man himself.

Suddenly a contraction hits her. The hot springs and the walk home have done what they were supposed to do. She clutches her stomach and takes a few deep breaths, with a quick glance at the man still lying motionless on the ground.

'Not now, little one. Please, not now,' she mumbles to herself.

With some more deep breaths the contraction subsides. She quickly takes in her surrounds, looking for something. Someone.

'Alligator. Alligator? Here, boy,' she whispers.

She gives a little whistle, then swiftly turns back to the black man. No movement from him, thank goodness. She looks out through the gap in the thicket. Only the family knows this thoroughfare. But there is no movement, no faithful dog trotting home with his tail between his legs, hoping his master will not be too stern about his absence. The only thing coming is a storm. Dark clouds build in the distance.

Molly attempts to call the dog again, frustrated now, and through clenched teeth.

'Alligator!! Where are ya? Ya bloody mongrel dog!'

There's a sound at the edge of the shanty. Molly turns with hope in her eyes, but it is short-lived on seeing who stands there.

'Been called so on many an occasion, missus. Sorry I'm not the *dog* you require.'

A swagman. He looks to be about sixty-five years old, give or take a few years either side, but fit and strong considering. He wears an old, worn, dirty three-piece suit, giving the impression he might once have had money, but more than likely not. It's his boots that give him away: they are soleless. The laces circle under his feet and are tied across the top of the boots. Trying to give himself some status with a pair of shoes.

Molly takes in the swagman slowly, giving her mind time to settle, but her heart beats hard and fast in her chest. In a split second, she thinks, *What the hell is goin' on here? Were my past days of good luck an illusion? I'm no Christian, but dear Lord – or any greater power for that matter – if ya listenin', I need ya strength.* She eyes her intruder: well, the conscious one. *Bloody hell – two of the bastards to deal with! Each as bad as the other.*

Molly knows the swagmen around these parts are not to be trusted. She's had her fair share of run-ins with these rogue sundowners and has run quite a few off her property. They come at sunset, trying not to hit the same property in succession, with desperate pleas for food and a bed, standing over the 'lady of the house'. They know who has a husband and when he is away: they're not as stupid, senile or caring as they make out.

With her shotgun aimed straight at the swagman, Molly stands strong. The swaggie quickly turns his focus to the black on the ground, hoping to take the attention off himself. 'He dead, missus?'

'You will be if ya don't state ya business, sundowner.'

The swagman introduces himself with a tip of his hat: 'Thomas McNealy, me lady.' He takes a flamboyant bow.

'Ain't no lady, just a drover's wife. State ya business!' Molly snaps back.

McNealy informs her that she might have scored herself a reward. Molly hasn't time for roundabout chitchat, and tells him so. The swaggie points to the Aboriginal man, still unconscious on the ground, and says, 'Felon on the run, missus! Murder. Murderer! Here on ya doorstep.' He points to the black again, placing sole blame, and with great conviction.

Molly probes for more information; she needs to know the details for her safety. 'Murder? Who?' Her voice rises an octave with curiosity.

McNealy continues with grand theatrics now: he knows he has her attention. 'The whole district is on the lookout! Be crawlin' with troopers any minute now.'

Molly's back straightens, her thoughts race, and for a split second she lets her guard down. The swaggie takes a step forward. Molly snaps back to her reality, raising her gun. 'Who was murdered?'

'A white woman, like you. On her own with her children. Mountain country.' McNealy delights in offering her this bit of information.

'Who?'

'A Missus Ulla Edwards and her wee ones. A week back now. Other side of the range. The hide of the murdering bastard. Such a prominent woman of the area.'

Molly is taken aback. Absentmindedly she lowers her gun, thinking about the tragedy. *Oh dear.* Molly did not know Ulla personally but had asked for favours when food was scarce. It was Danny who did the inquiring. Any death is sad and horrific, especially murder, especially a mother and her children. Proof, Molly knows, that danger can be anywhere and everywhere, and with the drover, her husband, away ...

McNealy sees her distraction and dives into his best performance yet. Pointing and with a slight skip in his step, he prances around the black man on the ground. 'Niggers! Savage bastards just like him. Might be him, wears the collar.'

Molly considers this and realises that yes, this could very well be true. He does wear the collar. For a fleeting moment, she shows her vulnerability. McNealy grasps the moment, theatrically leaping into his epilogue: 'Horrific! Rape, strangulation, the boys sodomised, and the girl drowned, life escapin' through sapphire-blue eyes ...'

Molly is caught up in his performance but her eyes narrow with caution. McNealy sees this and is quick to respond. 'So I'm told. The lengths people go to for detail. Those wee children. I think of yours – the wee girl, so precious.'

This last detail snaps Molly back to reality. What the hell was she thinking letting her guard down? She can only blame her hormones: *Standin' here listenin' to a rogue talkin' shite.*

She steps closer, her grip firm on her shotgun. 'What do you know of my children?'

McNealy knows he has overstepped the mark and quickly goes into submission, backing away like the dog he is, tail between his legs, asking the good lady for forgiveness.

But Molly steps up again. 'My children. What do you know of my children!'

McNealy, with his hat in his hands, tells Molly, 'You know the swagmen's trail. Round and round we go. Passed by here a few times. Kept me distance, good dog ya got there. Alligator, isn't it? Looked in, though. That's all. Truth, missus.'

'I wouldn't trust ya as far as I could spit. Get goin'!'

'Food and a little warmth of a comfortable bed is what I'll be askin' of ya.'

'If ya head due west and walk for half a day, you'll find a willin' woman and a comfortable bed.'

McNealy licks his lips. 'Ain't got no coin to pay.'

Molly cocks her gun. 'I'm sure you'll find a way.'

She doesn't falter in her defiance, but he is not moving either. Molly knows this game – she's played it before, and her poker face is strong. 'My Joe be home soon.' She holds his stare, giving him a second to take this in. 'Maybe ya seen his flock? Sheep. Due back to graze further downriver, along the low flats, before takin' 'em to the sale.'

A glint of mischief sparkles in McNealy's eyes. 'They're down and on their way.'

He's got her there, even if it is the truth or a lie, and Molly is reminded this could – no, this will – get dangerous. But as she contemplates her position she's hit with another contraction. She grabs her stomach, doubling over in pain. Seizing on her vulnerability, the swaggie rips the shotgun from her hands.

'Please, don't shoot! My children!'

Suddenly the black man jumps up, wielding Molly's axe, which has been hidden beneath him. Nursing his injury, exhausted and in pain, he swings it at the swaggie. Molly quickly gets out of the way, not sure who to run from. In her confusion she trips and falls heavily on her stomach. She groans, overwhelmed with pain.

The swaggie sidesteps just as the axe comes down, cutting deep into the chopping block. In the mayhem, McNealy drops the shotgun and it misfires, hitting no one. Molly manages to scramble after it, dragging herself across the ground.

The black hits the swaggie with a backhander, knocking him a little senseless. He tries to pull the axe free as the swaggie comes at him, grabbing him from behind and plunging his fingers deep into the wound on the black man's lower back. The black man lets out a yell that could wake the dead and collapses from the pain, pulling the axe free as he falls. He lies on the ground in agony but still clutching the axe to his chest should the swaggie attempt to come at him.

Molly attempts to reload the shotgun but is hit with another contraction and can only focus on her deep breaths. She fails to reload, dropping the bullet. The rogue swagman runs off, knowing he's outnumbered. The black man sucks in deep breaths, trying to bring his pain under control. His wound has opened up and bleeds.

When Molly tries to get up a guttural groan escapes her. She's in labour, but something isn't right. The Aboriginal man sees her distress. He gets up, axe in hand, and staggers towards her. Molly stiffens with fear – she can't do a thing! Her body locks in spasm with fear and labour pains. Afraid, she cowers, throwing an arm over her head in a desperate attempt to protect herself. 'My children! Please!'

I've never been so helpless in all my life and I can't do a thing about it! My mind races, flashin' images of my children, as my womb tears with life tryin' to escape. And yet my untimely death is here, now, before me. I am simply wrung out. I shut my eyes and hope that it is swift.

The black man stops, then turns and buries the axe back into the chopping block in a gesture meant to tell her he means no harm and has no intention of hurting her.

Molly manages to stand, and then her water breaks. She lifts her skirt and sees a wet patch at her feet. She can't believe it: it wasn't supposed to happen like this. Another contraction. She can't help but push. She feels between her legs and is devastated: 'Oh no, a foot.'

The black man steps attentively towards her, lowering his head, submitting.

Another contraction rips through Molly's body, and through clenched teeth, she says, 'Go! Get!'

The black stranger does not move or look up but offers his hand: a simple and kind gesture of help.

Molly's mind races. Through her laboured breaths she manages,

'A white woman … lettin' a black man touch her … is bad enough … let alone deliver her baby!'

In this moment of madness and mayhem Molly goes with the only option she feels she has. She brings the shotgun up like a bat, swings it with all her might and knocks him out cold. He drops with a thud.

THIRTEEN

Sergeant Nate Clintoff sighs to himself, *Bloody hell.* He looks utterly uncomfortable and out of place as he stands on the front lawn of the Edwards property with storm clouds building overhead. He pulls at the collar of his official sergeant's uniform, undoing the top button. Uptight and flustered, with his pith helmet tucked under his arm, he dabs at the sweat on his brow. Not because it is hot – winter is coming to the mountain country and there is already snow on the mountaintops – but because he is standing over the dead bodies of Mrs Ulla Edwards and her three children, laid out in wooden caskets. In disbelief and truly saddened, he looks away. This is not the first job he thought he would be presiding over in Australia. He knew there would be a few rough nights to deal with at the Stanlow Inn when the big droves came through Everton, or when the sales were on – but murder? An entire young family, on the sleepy slopes of this quaint, quiet mountain country?

When they offered Nate the position they made it sound easy, painting a grand picture of Australian life in the Snowy Mountains of the alpine country, the landscape picturesque and his duties light. A great place to raise a family. Skiing in the winter months when things are quiet. When Nate said yes to the position, crimes of this kind were the furthest thing from his mind. But here he is in the middle of a multiple-murder investigation. And, to say the least, he's a little lost.

He has no back-up or official support on the ground bar one – his assistant, Trooper Spencer Leslie, aged thirty-five and assigned to desk duties because his 'skills are not up to par'. And it will be days before reinforcements arrive.

Coming to Australia and to the mountain country was supposed to be a safe place for my son to grow up. To fulfil the promise to my dear wife of more children, me not having to worry about her safety at home alone, poring over her notebook, lost in her writing for her women's journal. Angst over my young son playing outside in the fresh air, lost in his imagination ...

I picture Louisa's beautiful smile, her contagious energy as I look down at the lifeless woman at my feet – someone's wife and mother. And looking back at Frank Edwards I see a man who is deeply hurting. I can't help but think, *This could have been my family.*

On the verandah of the Edwards' now-boarded-up home, Father McGuinness, a large, jolly seventy-year-old, comforts Frank. Trooper Leslie, a small-framed man with glasses, Nate's hardworking, very studious and attentive assistant, stands with them, taking notes and drawing a detailed description from Frank's words.

'His nose is narrow.' Spencer applies the note.

Father McGuinness asks, 'What are your intentions?'

Frank clears his throat. 'Melbourne. Nothing here for me now.'

'But this is your great-grandfather's property. Your grandfather Charles turned this place around. The town needs you.'

'Sorry, Father, but right now that is not my priority.'

Nate crouches down at Ulla's open casket, rubbing at his temple. His nose twitches with the scent of death. He considers the smell, then shakes off the thought. Where does he begin? He's been thrown into the deep end here, all right. From behind him comes a voice: 'If I may, sir, I'd say it would be good to get goin'.'

It's the undertaker, sixty-five years old, very tall, very skinny and looks like death warmed up himself. Nate takes no heed. He has a closer look at the bruising on the dead woman's neck. She's been strangled. *Who could do such a thing?* Nate notes that on the left side of her neck the bruising is darker, indicating the hold was stronger on that side: the murderer, left-handed – or perhaps an injury or a deformity to his right hand making it weaker? He jots this down in his notebook. There on the page is the description of how the children were murdered and taken advantage of.

Trooper Leslie joins his sergeant. He makes an adjustment to his drawing and stands dutifully waiting for further instruction. Finally, a curt Nate instructs, 'Get these bodies onto the wagon.'

The undertaker eagerly strides over to help. He and the trooper start with the three children. They slide the caskets onto the tray of the 'flat-back Larry', an open-tray wagon pulled by four horses, then come back for Ulla. The undertaker secures the lid and inquires as to the whereabouts of Sergeant Clintoff's wife. Nate is taken aback by the question. The undertaker nods towards the horizon, where a ferocious storm has broken. Lightning cracks and races across the sky, electrifying the air.

Nate hasn't seen a storm like this before. It rages in the distance. He watches, captivated by its beauty and harshness and the velocity of its build. Is this a sign of life to come?

'Hittin' the edge of town pretty hard,' the undertaker comments, interrupting Nate's thoughts. His fascination gives way to worry: Louisa and Samuel are home alone.

Louisa Clintoff swings a wet blanket at the flames eating at the base of a dead tree in the back corner of her property. The lightning strikes Nate has witnessed across the range have ignited the tree. The rain buckets down around her and her backyard is looking like a river. She struggles to lift the weight of the wet blanket but manages to extinguish the last flame.

Behind her a spooked horse gallops in a holding yard, stopping short of smashing through the fence. Louisa is fatigued by her efforts containing the fire and her words come back to haunt her: 'I'm looking forward to the challenges of life on the land.'

She dismisses the thought, gathers up her wet dress, puts on her determined face and marches across the yard to the horse. She crawls through the fence but gets caught up in it. Exasperated, she pulls at her snagged dress; it rips away and she falls in the process into a big muddy puddle. *Oh dear, what a sight I must be,* she thinks, as she wipes at the mud splashed on her face. She's not sure if she should laugh or cry.

Picking herself up, she tries to get the horse back into the barn. She waves her arms up and down, making herself bigger. She recalls Nate saying something like a calming 'Whoa, whoa,' so she mimics that and continues the flapping arm action. Miraculously, the horse settles.

'Well, I'll be. It works!' she says aloud. The horse is now staring down at her. She waves her arms and makes the sound again and manages to turn the horse. It gallops into the barn. With all her remaining strength, she pushes the double doors closed and secures the latch and leans against them, beat but proud of her efforts, wringing wet and exhausted but smiling a wide, satisfied grin.

With another bolt of lightning and massive crack of thunder she screams and races inside. Samuel stands at the back window laughing and clapping as his mother falls over in the same muddy puddle as she scrambles back through the fence. Defeated, she rolls over on her back, the cold rain hitting her face, and laughs and laughs. Life in Australia! A great story to write home to her parents about. *And add to my journal!* And with that she is up and away to get on with it, slipping at least three more times before reaching her back door.

The men have finished laying the Edwards' caskets, together with those of the two elderly Chinese hired-help, on the tray of the wagon, securing the pine coffins with rope. Nate and Spencer Leslie stand behind Frank Edwards, who stands alongside Father McGuinness as he conducts a prayer over the caskets. Frank's head is bowed, his shoulders slumped and shaking with emotion. The prayer is finished with the sign of the cross and the other men walk away, giving Frank a final moment alone with his deceased family.

Nate pulls Trooper Leslie away to talk privately. 'Missus Joe Johnson. Further south. I'm worried about her. She's alone – vulnerable and in a delicate condition.'

Father McGuinness can't help but overhear as he heads for the front of the undertaker's wagon. 'Nothing delicate about our mountain women.' The local men chuckle.

'Beg your pardon, Father McGuinness?' Nate is curious.

'Like I said the other night when you dropped her children off, Molly Johnson grew up out here. She knows the ways of these parts. Crack shot, too.'

'There is a murderer on the loose,' Nate chides.

Father McGuinness labours under his own weight as he climbs up into the wagon. Nate continues, 'I wish for no further harm to any woman or child—'

'Get home to your wife, sergeant.' They all look to the horizon, the rain falling and the lightning bouncing around the sky. 'She's your priority tonight.' Father McGuinness nods to the undertaker, who gathers up the reins. He looks back to Nate, and adds, 'And I'm not just talking about the storm.'

The undertaker snaps the reins and the horse and wagon slowly move off. Frank's wagon follows behind and Spencer Leslie sets off after it on foot.

Nate calls after him, 'Trooper Leslie?' Spencer reluctantly turns back to his commanding officer. 'Quickest way to the Johnsons' from here?'

Spencer quickly replies, his feet stumbling over rocks on the track: 'Over that hill and down the range on the other side, sir. Which I would not recommend. Not with a storm like that coming, sir. A local mountain man wouldn't do it.' He salutes and runs after the wagons, jumping onto Frank's wagon for a ride back to town.

Nate thinks on this. He looks towards the savage storm in the distance, knowing his wife and son are alone. He mounts his horse but charges towards the hill Spencer pointed out. He gallops up and over the rise and down the other side, digging his heels into his horse's flanks encouraging it to go faster. They approach a steep drop, but the horse won't go. It stops suddenly and Nate almost falls off. The horse dances around, stepping high and away from the steep drop, refusing to go any further. Finally, Nate settles the horse, turning it away from the drop.

He takes in the vastness of the land. He has seen nothing like it before: its beauty, its complexity and its danger, all laid out before him.

A crash of thunder directly above startles the horse and man. Nate, defeated by nature, turns the horse for home and heads back up the incline, hoping his wife and son are inside safe and sound.

FOURTEEN

Fat raindrops fall from the sky, hitting the black man in the face. His eyes flutter open. He lifts his head to look around, his vision blurred. There is something before him. From the blow to his head, through his daze and stupor, what he sees are obscure, fractured impressionistic images: a gaping mouth, hands reaching, arching back, twisted body and panic-stricken eyes.

Resting his head back down, he rubs where the shotgun connected. It hurts. He closes his eyes, trying to find his focus. *What the bloody hell just happened? How long have I been out? Thank the old people for the rain, which will wash away my tracks and scent ... Bloody hell, my head hurts ...*

Opening his eyes, he finds his vision much clearer. He lifts his head again to see lying before him the white woman. *The bitch that hit me! She's on the ground? In labour!* Molly's screams are muffled to the Aboriginal man as he comes to his senses. He tries to shake out the ringing in his ears.

Molly is in a great deal of pain. She holds her stomach. *Oh my God, this pain! I haven't experienced anythin' like this! I'm dyin'!* Through gritted teeth she screams, 'Heeeeelllppp!'

Groggily, the black man tries to get up. His vision swirls as he stands upright. Molly is desperate, her hands outstretched to him, grateful he has woken. But he could still kill her. He staggers towards her, coming around to stop at her feet, and takes in her situation: there between her legs, Molly's undergarments now removed, is a baby's leg and some of its lower body. This doesn't look good for either mother or child.

He wipes at the rain dripping from his face, expressionless. He picks up the shotgun and the dropped bullet, wiping off the wet and mud from the shell. As he reloads the shotgun, he watches Molly convulsing. She pleads, 'Please ... don't shoot ... my ... *CHILDREN*!' just as a contraction hits and the urge to push becomes too great.

The rain hammers down.

Early-morning mist hovers over the land and a light frost covers the ground. There's an eerie stillness in the air. The white sallees and snow gums look like spirits caught in the landscape.

Molly stands on her verandah, silent and still, her Cowles & Dunn aimed straight at the black man who cowers in the far corner. She steps forward to stand over him. He stares up the barrel of her shotgun. Pale and clammy, her stern face peers down at him. He stares straight back at her, too afraid to move. His hands and shirt are covered in dry blood. Molly's blood.

Her baby belly is gone. She shifts her weight, unsteady on her feet. There is a moment of tense stillness between them. Molly licks her dry lips to speak, her voice hoarse: 'You saved my life.'

The black man exhales slowly, glad she has spoken and didn't decide to pull the trigger. The tension between them still hangs thick, each unsure of the other.

'What were ya intendin' to do with my axe?' The black man gives nothing away. 'Well?' Nothing again. 'You wear the collar?'

'I did not do those things that swaggie said.'

Molly is taken aback; he speaks perfect English – no myall talk from him. Quizzically, she asks, 'You schooled?'

He just holds her stare, knowing others have lost their lives admitting to this.

'A schooled black is a danger in itself,' she states.

Molly sways. She leans into the verandah post for support. Her questions come fast now. She wants to get to the bottom of why he is at her home and then she needs him gone. He fires back his replies, nothing to hide.

'What were ya intendin' to do with my axe?'

'Take the collar off – try to.'

'Ya was facin' towards my home.'

'Food.'

'Puttin' ya'self in danger.'

'Need food, missus. Been runnin' for days. Carryin' this wound. This.' He indicates the collar. 'Heard ya comin', laid down there. Hopin' ya wouldn't shoot.'

She pauses thoughtfully, then says, 'Knowin' I was alone.'

Guilty. He looks down at his hands covered in her dried blood. Molly's got him there. She looks out at the soft muddy ground in her front yard, tracks everywhere, his tracks, clearly showing yesterday's activities. They tell the story if you know how to read them, and Molly does – one of her gifts.

'Ya need to go—'

'Bury that little girl. Least I can do for ya, missus.'

'You owe me nothin',' she says defiantly

But he knows that helping to bury the baby girl is the proper thing for him to do. 'Sorry for your loss, missus.'

She looks him up and down, her lips pursed with distaste. 'It's the way of life out here. Everythin''s a gamble.' She knows this too well – and the gamble includes him. Molly needs him to leave. 'The mountains are rife with trouble, if what the swaggie said is true. And if he goes to town lookin' for that reward, I'm gonna have troopers on my doorstep – and that is somethin' I don't want or need.' *Especially now,* she thinks.

The Aboriginal man hears her concern. 'If he was a decent man he would be.' This is what he is hoping – he needs time to rest and for his wound to heal.

Sweat beads on her brow and Molly pats at it. She is looking very unwell. She begins to sway, her breathing becoming uneasy. 'Why should I trust ya?'

He looks at her sincerely, and says, 'You have no reason to, missus.'

Another moment passes between them, Molly's uneasiness wavering a little. The black man has no choice but to offer up another option: 'Help me with the collar and I'll be on my way.'

Molly is desperately trying to keep her wits about her. 'That's government property. You are theirs.'

'Never!' he snaps back, with hatred in his tone. This puts Molly on guard.

'Ya must've done somethin' wrong to be wearin' it.'

'My only crime, missus, is existin' whilst black.'

This sits heavy between them. Molly understands what he means. She has seen this sort of treatment growing up. The blacks around here are still blamed for everything. Not that there are many left. Most have been arrested and imprisoned or moved on – 'dispersed', as some would say – and at present the whites have unofficial government permission to shoot any black on sight.

'Please, missus, I mean you no harm.' He looks around the yard, searching urgently for another angle with which to gain time. He spots the woodheap in urgent need of maintenance. 'I can fell a tree for you. Stack the woodheap. Level the ground there, though, don't want snakes getting in under.'

'Least of my worries,' she says, dabbing at her brow again. The black man looks desperately at her, knowing his fate is in her hands. Molly tries to keep herself together. Her vision is blurring and her breathing is shallow. Then she faints, landing at his feet.

FIFTEEN

Trooper Spencer Leslie tacks up to a noticeboard a stencil copy of the excellent drawing he's done from Frank Edwards' description of the Aboriginal man wanted for the murder of the Edwards family. It's an uncanny depiction of the black man taking shelter with Molly – although Spencer has taken liberties, giving his subject the enraged eyes of a murderous savage.

Sergeant Nate Clintoff sits perched on the corner of his desk, reading from a telegram. 'Bodies. Stop. A Trooper, Native Policeman found. Stop. Three weeks ago. Stop. North of Victorian border. Stop. Moving Native prisoner.' Nate holds the telegram, appalled, tightening his fist around it. 'Black Tracker says prisoner killed them. He also said the prisoner is wounded, lower back. Stabbed.'

He and Spencer look at the wanted poster of the murderous black. Nate rubs at his temples, sighing with frustration. 'Eight people dead. What would make him come back up into the mountains?'

'Probably a Walgalu or Ngarigo man. A local man.'

Nate remembers sitting out in Louisa's garden, reading. Finding some quiet time while Samuel has his mid-morning nap. Brief after brief, page after page preparing for his work in Australia. Louisa was out this morning with her mother. He was quite intrigued with the local clans, tribes and nearby nations' names, their boundaries and areas they consider sacred. Reminded him of the Scottish heritage practices. Then he found a statement in bold print that made his stomach churn:

> *It is essential to know the myalls if we are to disperse of them from the district. They do slow up progress, and are a nuisance to the new settlers and landholders and their livestock. All assistance warranted by settlers to help clear their way, should be guaranteed.*

'I'd advise a raiding party, sir,' Spencer Leslie offers, cutting through Nate's thoughts. Nate looks at him, appalled. 'If we don't, the locals will. They won't spare the gins or children.'

'Innocent people will die!'

'Blacks, sir.'

Good Lord, the attitudes here! There is much I need to learn. Nate swallows his displeasure.

Trooper Leslie suggests they bring troopers and trackers from Jarren's Outpost, the most southern outpost to the Victorian border. He goes to the wall map and circles the area. Nate follows the trajectory they would come. *The squadron could pass through the Johnsons' property – this is good*, he thinks.

As if reading his mind, Spencer says, 'Molly Johnson will be checked on, sir. But it will still be two days before they can get to her. And that's only if they leave the outpost immediately.' He allows a moment of thought before he continues, 'Our responsibility to her welfare would then be over, sir.'

'I'm hoping her husband will be home by then,' Nate says. He looks to the northern border closest to the mountain range, remembering from his briefing *the blacks use the mountains to travel by*. Spencer follows Nate's gaze. Knowing what he is thinking, he points out Milbaral: 'It's the most northern outpost closest to the mountain range.'

Spencer knows the ways of the blacks well, and the lie of the land. He has lived and worked in the area for some time. His father, a retired trooper, pulled strings to get his son the position he now holds. Spencer was bent on serving his country but his poor physical coordination set him back. His clerical skills and outstanding drawing ability put him in good stead for a management position in the sleepy outpost of Cresthill.

Nate circles both the outposts, joining their trajectories to include the circled Johnson property on the map. 'Get a telegram to both posts asking for their help with trooper support and an indication of when they think they might move out. If it's not immediately, you'll need to take a little ride, trooper.'

'Riding's not my strongest point, sir,' Trooper Leslie replies, with an embarrassed smile. 'It would have been in your brief, sir.'

Nate looks at him disapprovingly. Spencer tries to save face: 'And tonight, the town will be totally out of control, sir – you'll need me here.'

There's no denying that. Nate has been warned about the night after the big sale. He dismisses Spencer with an order to get copies of the drawing tacked up around town as soon as possible. He takes one himself and leaves.

Nate walks down the main street of Everton. New construction lines the outer streets, which excites him. A new town. His town. He exchanges pleasantries with well-to-do high-society outsiders, here for the sale and not enjoying the muddy puddles left from the earlier downpour. He stops to admire the newly erected town sign. 'Everton' is burnt into the wood panel with 'June 1893' beneath it.

From behind, a polished voice calls to him. 'Clintoff? Sergeant Nathaneal Clintoff?'

Nate turns to see across the street a very dignified gentleman with a cane. The gentleman waves him over. Nate obliges, stepping around a few big puddles as he skips across the way. The man holds out his hand and introduces himself.

'Good afternoon. Judge Alfred Eisenmangher, District Court.'

Nate realises who this is immediately. He straightens up and takes the man's hand in a firm grasp. 'Pleasure, Your Honour.'

The judge, who is about seventy-five years old and a stern authoritarian, tips his hat. 'If you make it past Sunday, I'll officially swear you in on Monday,' he jokes, breaking the ice.

'You may as well officially open the town, too,' Nate says, tongue in cheek, as this is also on the agenda.

Eisenmangher smiles. 'If I get a good price for my sheep, I'll think about it.' They chuckle, sharing pleasantries. Then the judge takes a serious tone: 'A little more than you bargained for, walking straight into a multiple-murder investigation?' Not giving Nate time to respond, he continues: 'We make an example of anyone who commits murder from here on in.'

Nate nods, agreeing. 'Understood, sir.'

The judge clears his throat for his spiel to come: 'The Edwards are a prominent family in the high country. They've been here since the 1820s, our founding fathers. It's their money progressing Everton to further development.' He pauses for dramatic effect. 'If they leave, they take their money with them and the town will fold – and my retirement plan falls over. Find Missus Edwards and her children's killer or killers. That should be your only concern at this time, sergeant.'

'As we speak, sir, I'm waiting on word from outposts to the north and south for trooper support.'

The judge nods his approval. 'Welcome to Everton.' With that, he tips his hat and heads across the street.

Nate sighs, worry in his eyes, feeling yet further pressure to solve the Edwards' murders: his reputation and the future of the town weigh heavily on solving the crime and making an example of the murderer. He has to show he has control. Keen to look the part, he squares his shoulders and straightens his back, bringing his body to his full six feet four inches. His physique is impressive. He strides off down the street with determination in his step.

Locals add the final touches to their stalls. Nate passes a small sideshow consisting of a merry-go-round, a knock-'em-down stall and a boxing tent. He sees a healthy and fit Aboriginal man, possibly one of the many Aboriginal boxers who work for the sideshows that travel the country – a way of working and escaping poverty on the outskirts of towns, displaced. The Aboriginal man places a big bass drum on the tent platform; this will be used to drum up business later, like a heartbeat, boomp-bomp, boomp-bomp, ringing out, echoing off the nearby ranges, calling all and sundry to take on the tent-show fighters.

A thought crosses Nate's mind: *I should come back to them. Ask a few questions. Show the poster, at least. A blackfellow knows a blackfellow, so I've read.*

But for now he really needs to get to the stockyards to find Joe Johnson, Molly's husband. He takes a left turn, walking away from the main street and straight towards the gathered crowd. The holding yards have been renovated, with freshly erected wooden fence posts and rails where needed. A brand-new sign above reads 'The Charles Edwards Saleyards' in honour of Charles Edwards, who first came to the area in the 1820s looking for better pastures to graze his sheep.

As Nate gets closer, the stench of the livestock drifts on the slight breeze, and there is an energy in the air as well: testosterone, and plenty of it.

Reaching the saleyards, Nate is taken aback by the sheer number of livestock, and stockmen, businessmen and farmers perched on rails looking down into the holding pens at their prospective buys. The auctioneers walk the top rails giving information on the quality and breeds. The area is buzzing, filled with business, laughter, arguments and bleating sheep. Stockmen of all ages and sizes place their saddle blankets and saddles on the fences to air. A few of them put out some feed; a few comb their horses down and check the hooves. Groups are standing around telling yarns from the drove they've just completed. The adventures in these yarns will carry and grow, becoming more daring over the next few days. A few men argue over money owed.

Nate heads towards the first group of stockmen he comes across; they aren't as boisterous as the others. They stand at the side of the yards, filling a water trough for their horses. There are a couple of Aboriginal stockmen with them who might be able to help in identifying the black man on the poster.

'Morning, gentlemen. Nate Clintoff, sergeant.'

The stockman standing closest to Nate turns and offers his hand. He's the head stockman of his team, about fifty-five years in age.

'Bruce Longley.'

They shake. Nate doesn't waste any time and gets straight to his point: 'I'm looking for Joe Johnson.'

'Not in my team, sergeant. Any of you know Joe Johnson?' Bruce asks his crew. Two of the three stockmen look up from what they are doing, shaking their heads. Bruce throws a look at a shorter, smaller-framed stockman, just a boy. 'Marti?'

Marti stands up from tying off his duffel bag. 'I think he's with Robert Parsen's crew. They've left already.' The slightly feminine, higher-pitched voice throws Nate. He looks closer and sees that Marti is in fact a woman in her early forties.

She offers him her hand. 'Martha Murray. Marti preferred.'

Feeling slightly foolish, Nate takes her hand and they shake. 'They've left? Where to? Do you know?' She smiles, pointing to the hotel across the way, the Stanlow Inn. They watch as three stockmen reach the establishment and are immediately surrounded by ladies of the night. They hang off the men like leeches, knowing all too well that this is their night to make some coin.

'The big bloke out front with the red beard, that's Robert Parsen, and his little sidekick is John McPharlen. The other must be ya Joe Johnson. Those three are pretty close.'

The three men enter the inn's swinging doors and disappear into a dingy smoke-filled room. Nate watches, knowing he won't be getting to them for a while at least.

One of the Aboriginal stockmen says in language to Marti: '*Njurrambai wadjbala bala-bala Yaraman.*' (That's Joe Johnson's horse. Heard the white men talkin' about it.)

'*Wur.*' (Good.) Marti nods in appreciation for the information. 'And, that's his horse.' She points to the agitated chestnut mare in the other yard. 'One of the boys here heard 'em talkin' about it.'

The mare runs back and forth along the fence, looking out to the mountains – at freedom, perhaps? Bruce pipes up, 'She looks keen to get home.'

Nate offers a lame smile. 'I was hoping Joe Johnson was too.'

'A man's gotta have a fuck, a feed and a fight before facin' the family.' Marti's language takes Nate by surprise. Bruce gives her a disapproving look. Feigning bashfulness, Marti takes her husband's arm and says, 'Well, some do, my dear.'

Bruce gives Nate some advice: 'If ya wanna get any sense out of 'em or want 'em to see reason, I'd wait a bit.' He quickly adds, 'It wasn't his family that was murdered, was it?'

Nate tells him it wasn't, but he's hoping Joe Johnson is heading home sooner rather than later. He adds, 'I haven't been able to get away to see if his wife is all right. I'm especially worried for her being in the district where the murders took place.' *But at least Joe's in town and will head home eventually,* he thinks.

He takes the poster from his pocket and shows it to the two Aboriginal stockmen. They look at it closely, speaking softly to each other in language. Bruce interrupts them: 'Speak up, Jimmy James.'

The stockman removes his hat to speak. 'Nuthin', boss. Don't know him.'

Nate takes the poster and places it back in his pocket as he contemplates his next move.

Sixteen

A large piece of medium-rare steak sizzles beside Molly's bed. The plate rests on a homemade side table, steam rising off it. Molly stirs. Fractured, obscure images flash before her eyes, too confusing to make any clear sense. Is it the horror of yesterday or something else driving these nightmares? Suddenly she springs awake and sits bolt upright. She looks around to get her bearings and sees her shotgun lying beside her on the bed. *Where's the black man? What's he up to?* She looks around and sees him sitting on the floor near the stove, eating, his back to her.

The Aboriginal man has finished off the last morsels of his meal, sucking a small bone clean. He needed that. A look of satisfaction crosses his face as he pockets the bone. He feels the muzzle of the gun on his scalp and surrenders, raising his hands. Behind him stands Molly, her shotgun aimed at the back of his head. A thought crosses his mind: *If this is my last meal, it was bloody good.*

'Get up and get outside!' Molly orders. He does as he is told.

Outside, Molly holds the axe up high. The Aboriginal man's head is on the chopping block. She brings the axe down: *bang*, straight on the hinge of the man's collar. It falls away. With the iron collar in his hand, he springs up from his kneeling position before the chopping block, grateful.

They hold each other's stare. 'Thank you, missus,' he says, indicating the collar. 'Thank you.'

Molly looks at him wearily. She is not sure if she has done the right thing. *Blast it! What the hell have I done?* When he had the collar on, she had some control over him. This could mean trouble for her, but he's already had ample opportunity to kill her if he so desired. And if he's wearing the collar and anyone comes here, that collar will bring them both undone. Other than his injury, he's a fit, capable man, and she needs help. With the trauma of the breech birth Molly's not well and there is only so much Danny will be able to do. Freeing him – she did owe the black man that for his trouble, helping with her stillborn baby girl, and essentially saving her life.

He looks at her, questioning. Molly finds her strength and stands tall, bringing her shotgun up and across her body. All she really wants is to go to bed for a few days. With her bravado returning comes her confirmation for his questioning eyes: 'One night. Fell a tree, and ya need to be gone.'

'Two, full moon by then. Good to walk by.'

Molly can't believe his audacity. 'Give ya an inch and you'll take a bloody mile!'

She tries another tack. 'My husband be home soon.'

'And your children?' He innocently asks. This puts Molly on guard. She points her shotgun straight at him. 'What do you know of my children?'

'Noticed the little stretcher-beds along the wall. That's all.'

'They're none of your business.'

Silence between them, Molly holding her ground. 'Cross me and I'll kill ya. Shoot ya where ya stand and bury ya where ya fall.'

He nods his understanding, believing she'll do just that.

'Bury that deep,' she says, indicating the collar. They look at each other, knowing they are now in this together. Molly has damaged government property to release a prisoner. 'Best ya stay out of sight.'

He nods, appreciative. 'Yes, boss,' the black man replies, dropping his head in respect. Molly knows this action, having seen it as a little girl; the blacks do it all the time. Doesn't mean much, because they can still be rogues. That's what Molly remembers.

'My husband's the boss. I'm just a drover's wife. Now, get to buryin' that collar and diggin' the grave. I'll go and say my goodbyes.'

'Good to do that, missus.'

Molly ignores him and goes inside. As she steps across the threshold, her guard slips away and the agony on her face shows just how ill she really is.

'Can I wash up before we bury the little one? I would like to be respectful . . .'

Molly turns back to him, angered by his talking. *Is he stallin'? Is he playin' at somethin'?* She gives him a once-over, then realises he's covered in dried blood and mud – another dead giveaway.

She nods. 'Be quick about it.'

The Aboriginal man steps forward and offers his hand, saying, 'Yadaka. Of the Guugu Yimithirr adopted Ngarigo.' He attempts a smile. His teeth are perfect.

Molly doesn't take his hand but says, 'Missus Joe Johnson.' With her gun, she indicates for him to get around the back. She waits for him to disappear around the side of her shanty, then looks to the front yard, at the ground, tracks everywhere in the soft mud, and exhales deeply. Nothing she can do about it now, too exhausted and no dry dirt anyway to try to hide them with. She'll have to wait to cover them.

She heads inside, vanishing into the darkness of the shanty. The sound of the latch, locking.

*

It's mid-afternoon. Shadows start to creep across the front yard.

Molly's weathered homemade rocking chair gently rocks back and forth, with a slight wobble because of unevenness in one of the rails. She found the chair in parts during one of her lonely long walks. It must have fallen from someone's wagon. She carried the pieces home and set about putting it back together.

Molly loves this chair, with all its imperfections. In it she has rocked all her five children – well, six, including this one. She quietly hums a sorrowful tune. It's the old lament her da sang to her, 'Black Is the Colour'. The humming and creaking of her rocking chair become melodic. Molly's emotionless eyes stare off to nowhere. One worn hand softly taps the beat on the cloth bundle she has laid across her lap: her swaddled dead baby girl.

Yadaka appears at the side of the shanty, his clothes freshly washed and partly dried. There is still evidence of bloodstains, or stains of some sort. He carries a little makeshift coffin. He is struck by the devastating sight of Molly sitting on her verandah rocking with her newborn, the dead baby across her lap. There is a ... distance in Molly. There are no tears. Yadaka is curious. He has gathered she is a hard woman and has lived a hard life, but ... *This is her baby*.

He inches closer. Molly has not acknowledged him yet. He removes the little coffin lid. 'Missus?'

Absent-mindedly Molly turns and places the swaddled baby in the coffin without any further word. She turns away. Still no sign of emotion. Eventually, she speaks. 'I rode for nineteen miles with that dead baby boy in my arms. He was six months old. Didn't see a soul. My cow died then. I truly was alone.'

Yadaka looks to her, a little perplexed by the story she tells. But he dares not interrupt, sensing this is something she wants to share, perhaps?

'Joe gone, Queensland. Drovin'. Eighteen months. Just married. Me, sixteen years old.' Her breath catches.

'You right, missus?'

No response from Molly.

'Missus, shall I ...' He holds up the lid, asking whether he should close it over.

Molly goes to him, clenches her fist and places it gently on the baby's covered forehead. She blows through her fist.

Yadaka frowns with curiosity. He knows this action and what it means. *How does she know this?*

'So you are always with her,' he says to her.

'A gin showed me. She helped me bury my firstborn, Jack. She helped me bury my da, too. Cried a river, she did. Howlin' like the ragin' wind in a storm ... it's not like she knew him. And then before she left she did that to me, too. I liked it. That's why I do it. I knew it must have meant something like that – *always with you*.'

A comfortable silence sits between them for a moment, Molly and Yadaka in close proximity to each other. He is aware of it but doesn't want to disturb Molly, and the moment she is in. He can feel something is going on for her at this time.

'She frightened me a little, but ... there was also comfort and beauty to the ...?'

'Wailin',' Yadaka informs her. Molly just stares at him, oblivious almost. Feeling uncomfortable with their closeness and her vagueness, he adds, 'Sounds like Ginny May.' He's quick to add, 'I know whose country this is and who can do business on it. She is our medicine woman and she spoke of you. Two births.'

This gets Molly's attention. 'Joe Junior and Henry James,' she says wistfully.

Yadaka clears his throat, knowing what he is about to say will get a big reaction. 'And a no-good man.' He braces himself to be chastised. He knows he's crossed the line with this assumption.

'I'll get my hat,' she responds, then turns and heads inside, leaving Yadaka dumbfounded by her reaction.

Yadaka hopes that what he has said won't come back to haunt him, jeopardising his time here. He is intrigued with her story now. *Maybe she'll open up some more?* There is something about her, but he can't put his finger on it. It has been a long time since Ginny May told him that story – a story so dear to her that she would repeat it over and over whenever she had the chance. *Maybe . . . it is this woman?*

Yadaka hopes that after the burial Molly will not tell him to go. He knows he needs a little more time to recuperate from his injury, which still pains him. He managed to make a medicine of herbs and moss to help it heal but is depleted from weeks of walking over rough and dangerous terrain, exhausted by his ordeal with the law and the exertion of his escape. Yadaka is relieved that those days are behind him now. He's looking forward to a more restful, sound sleep tonight, his belly full: he knows there is plenty of meat here.

As Yadaka waits, he thinks back to his first meeting with Ginny May. He had been walking for many days following the mountain ranges – black man's thoroughfare, quickest way to travel across country.

Yadaka thought about his good fortune: an easy escape from a previous minder – or guardian, as Father Daniel Matthews called himself for all the young Aboriginal boys in his care. He was a good man, slightly eccentric, who ran a place for so-called wayward young black men in Echuca, Victoria. Yadaka had arrived there when he was about fifteen years old.

He'd been left stranded in Melbourne by the South African Fillis Circus and jailed for being destitute. When Yadaka was about twelve years old, he ran away from a disgruntled and violent employer who accused him of stealing his gold. So he stowed away on the big ship that had been harboured in the Cook Town port for over a week. He was drawn to the ship with all the strange animals. Being tired and hungry, he had lain down on some fresh hay to rest and fallen asleep, only to wake again on the high seas of the Pacific Ocean. He would tour the east coast of Australia with the circus for three years.

He was almost dead when Father Matthews collected him from Pentridge Prison. The dim candlelight shone across Yadaka's dark cell, waking him from possibly falling into his final sleep. Naked and cold, he slowly and steadily got up and walked to the little barred window and took the slice of bread from Matthews' hand. Yadaka was very grateful for the priest's help.

Father Matthews had a loving and attentive wife and daughter. Yadaka was trusted and given a place as a house black, keeping maintenance around the home. He was taught to read and write and enjoyed the music shared in church on Sundays and at the Matthews' home on Friday evenings. But he always yearned for his 'land', to get 'home' to his mother's country in Far North Queensland. He had a great urge to be back with his clan.

Yadaka attempted to run away many times but was always captured and brought back. At twenty-five years old he attempted to run again, and this time his escape was successful. As he walked through the mountain ranges working his way north, he stumbled across other clans walking the ranges. They were all heading in the same direction. Yadaka was well aware that you needed to be wary of approaching anyone outside your own tribe. Not being from this area was even more dangerous. He followed at a distance and finally arrived at a big gathering of nations, tribes and clans from all over.

It brought me great joy to see so many clansmen and women together. All those beautiful black faces still finding things in life to smile about. They gave me hope. I stayed on the perimeter and soon saw they were gathering for ceremony. Mobs were quick to get into the songs and dances for celebrating the gift of the bogong moth. To feast on the protein-filled moths was good at that time of year. Fattening everyone up for the approaching winter months. For my safety I quickly worked out who the hosting nation was and made myself known. I told them of my plight and the elders took council. A woman in her early sixties took a great interest in me. I was a little concerned that maybe she had plans to make me her husband – not that she was unattractive, but I was only there for a short time and needed to get back to my people, to my mother, if she was still alive. I missed her greatly – I had not seen her since I was twelve. Word came back that I could stay and I would be adopted by the woman. I was to call her *Njadjan*, 'Mother'. I was not sure why the woman had done this, but I was very grateful to be calling her mother.

Not long after, Yadaka understood the woman's motive. She had a story to tell, a story she held very dear but was forbidden to share with others in her clan. This yarn was considered bad luck or a no-good story. It was a story of treachery, broken lore and forbidden love. By adopting Yadaka as her son, his adopted mother, Ginny May, could share it with him. He was her chosen one to keep the story alive. He was now responsible for it. And maybe one day something would come of it.

All of a sudden, memories of the story come flooding back to Yadaka. They do not come in chronological order but in bits and pieces. It will take time for him to reconfigure it again. He will ask the ancestors for guidance. If Ginny May has passed on, maybe she will come to him in his dreams.

Just then Yadaka hears the back door of the shanty close. He quickly goes to join Molly but runs literally straight into Danny, who is loaded up with supplies.

Danny has been running at pace to get the supplies and a gift from Miss Shirley to his ma, desperate to see if he has a baby brother or sister.

Bang! Danny drops, hitting the ground hard. The supplies spill everywhere. Yadaka stumbles backwards. Danny picks himself up, slightly winded, but on seeing the black man he furiously propels himself at him, fists flying and calling, 'Ma!'

SEVENTEEN

Back in Everton, the main street is alive with action, and Nate Clintoff is in the thick of it. Clientele from the Stanlow Inn have gathered on the platform outside to cheer on their new upholder of Her Majesty's law.

Nate's clenched fist lands, packing quite a punch, on the jaw of a drunken stockman, who falls to the ground, out cold. Nate quickly turns, bobbing under the swinging arm of another. He counters with an uppercut to the jaw, sending that stockman stumbling arse-over-tit into a water trough.

Nate uses this moment to catch his breath. The last thread of his torn shirt gives way and falls away, exposing his chiselled chest. He rubs at his injured thigh. The fight looks to be over and he acknowledges the crowd with a nod. The cheering grows into thunderous applause. One of the ladies of the night lets rip with a wolf whistle. More cheering. Nate can't help but blush. He knows he had to show the town he can handle himself and won't be a pushover: it was Nate who threw the first punch to prove his point to the loud, obnoxious drunken stockman who was questioning his authority in the high country, and the gathering crowd were keen to see what the new sergeant had to offer.

A few of the working girls perched at the rail of the Stanlow give him the once-over. Bare-shouldered and muscular, Nate dusts down his pants. The women can't take their eyes off him. Their gaze falls to his tight arse, framed perfectly in his uniform pants, as he bends over to collect his shirt from the ground and tucks it into his back pocket. And to top it all off, there's his handsome jawline, which any woman would want to nuzzle. They all sigh simultaneously, whispering to each other, 'So he's the new law in town.'

One comments with a singsong cadence, 'He can arrest me anytime he likes.'

'He married, ya think?'

'Has that ever mattered?'

The girls burst out laughing, applauding Nate as he limps over to grab the stockman floating face down in the trough by the scruff of the neck to haul him out.

Trooper Spencer Leslie arrives, late as usual, fumbling with his wrist shackles. The crowd chuckles and waves him away. That's the usual reaction Spencer gets. No one applauds him.

Nate drags the other stockman, still knocked out, beside the water-drenched one, and Spencer shackles them together. There is a final cheer and another round of applause, the town's way of showing its approval. Nate smiles obligingly and takes a little bow, happy to play along. Spencer is impressed too, and joins in the clapping.

Trooper Leslie holds open the cell doors for Sergeant Clintoff as he heaves the two drunken stockmen in. They stumble and tumble onto the other drunken stockmen sprawled all over the cell floor.

'We're going to have to let a few go,' Spencer says, as he tucks a leg in so he can close the door. 'We've got to make room for tonight.'

Nate shakes his head in disbelief. Spencer Leslie had been right when he said the town was out of control on sale day. And there was still daylight in the sky. His decision not to ride out to Molly Johnson was a smart move.

Spencer Leslie has seen this level of drunkenness and debauchery many a time, and is an old hand at throwing drunken stockmen in the clink. Lock 'em up. Sober 'em up. Let 'em out to do the same thing again within a few hours. He's been posted at the Cresthill outpost in the Everton district for nearly nine years now and has been very happy with his desk job and running the little outpost. Nothing much happens. There was talk of town development for the area almost two decades back, but in his time the population has doubled. And with the livestock route bringing everyone to this point as a middle ground, talk came back on the table again for Cresthill Outpost to become a town. Spencer knew there would be a superior officer appointed to run the place, and he was fine with that. That was the kind of man he was. He'd also been fine for the 'girl of his dreams' to come from the other side of Australia: he saved for a whole year to pay her transport to bring her over, only for her to arrive and marry another.

Nate finishes buttoning his new shirt. Luckily, Louisa insists he always have a change of clothes on hand just in case. He is grateful that his wife thinks of everything. Out the back, he washes his face in the sink, tidies his hair, checks his grazed knuckles. The front door of the jailhouse swings open and in rushes one of the officials from the saleyard, panting heavily, sweat running from his brow. 'Sir, we have gentlemen drawing pistols at twenty paces. Dispute about the sheep just brought!' He swallows hard, hands on his hips and face distorted as he sucks in oxygen.

Nate and Spencer look at each other. 'Told you, sir,' Spencer says, shrugging. They both rush out the door.

EIGHTEEN

Sweet singing wafts on the light afternoon breeze. It's Danny. 'Her face is something wondrous fair ...'

Under the shade of a big old snow gum Molly, Danny and Yadaka stand within a rusty iron-fence enclosure – the family burial plot.

Danny's song continues: 'The purest smile and the gentlest of hands ...' He steals a side glance at the black man, curious but wary. 'I love the ground whereon she stands.' Danny's eyes shift quickly away when Yadaka looks over at him. Yadaka likes the boy, likes the fight in him and his loyalty to his ma. Danny would be about the same age as his eldest son.

In the fenced area, the graves are marked with homemade wooden crosses. The names are branded on them: *Jack 'Jock' Stewart, beloved father 1807–1869; Jack Joseph Johnson 1869*. There is also a large river rock with the name *Mary* chipped into it.

The beauty of Danny's voice would bring a tear to the eye of the hardest stockman: 'So fare thee well my own true love ...' Molly is still caught in her melancholy – she stares off to nowhere, lost, only slightly flinching at the hammering of the nails as Yadaka drives them into the little coffin, sealing the lid shut. He and Danny in rhythm with song and hammering, hauntingly beautiful but deeply distressing. Even Yadaka wipes away a tear.

Then, Molly finally speaks, breaking the tenderness of the moment with an abrupt and absurd question to her eldest boy: 'Joe Junior and Henry James behave for Miss Shirley?'

With tears in his eyes, Danny looks to his ma, dumbfounded. 'Good ... as gold found in Kiandra, Ma.' And then Molly leaves. Yadaka has finished the nailing of the coffin lid and looks up, puzzled by her outburst. They watch Molly walk away. Finally, Danny turns back to Yadaka. They eye each other, Danny shrugs his shoulders, and they both turn back to see Molly go in the back door of the shanty. Danny sighs, bringing their thoughts and attention back to the completion of the burial.

Yadaka takes a little homemade wooden cross, steps forward and drops to his knee to stake it into the ground. Danny grabs his arm. 'That's my job, mister.'

Yadaka nods, understanding completely. He hands Danny the cross and steps back. Danny mimics the black man's stance and drives the cross into the ground, pushing a handful of dirt up and around to secure it. It reads: 'Daisy Molly Johnson, 1893'.

Danny and Yadaka step back, both bowing their heads in respect – a sombre and serene moment shared between them, considering their first encounter with each other. Danny can't help but steal another glance at the black man. His curiosity is getting the better of him. Then Yadaka leaves, heading off into the scrub.

Danny watches the Aboriginal man walk away. He looks back to the shanty, his mother's whispered words to him as they walked to the family burial plot coming back to him: 'Keep ya distance. Stay away from him, Danny. We can't trust him. Besides, he has work to do. So, no flappin' ya trap – leave him be.'

But Danny's wonderment in this man gets the better of him. Fearing he might lose Yadaka in the scrub, Danny races off after him. Striding out over fallen branches, sidestepping around clumps of grass and leaping over a wombat burrow, he makes his charge to catch the black man up. And soon Danny is lost to the thicket.

Molly lies on her bed, facing the wall. She cradles herself, a tear rolling down her cheek. *Another lost ... buried. Perhaps for the best. So much could go wrong at this time, too much at stake with what I have done ... and with a newborn babe to deal with as well ... well, there's enough to consider and worry about with the others ...*

Finally Molly breaks, and silently, she sobs.

In a bush clearing, Danny tends a small fire. A billycan of water comes to the boil over red-hot coals. Danny slides a stick under the handle to safely lift it from the flames. He pours in some tea leaves and taps at the side of the billy to sink the leaves to the bottom.

Yadaka's voice comes from behind him. 'Thank you.'

Nervous and afraid, Danny steps back quickly and stumbles, nearly spilling the newly brewed hot liquid. Yadaka lets the moment pass. He doesn't move and doesn't look at the boy. He doesn't want to do anything to frighten him further.

'Join me?' Yadaka asks, pointing at the tea in the billy. Danny remembers his ma's warning: he was told to keep his distance.

'I'm not allowed to talk to strangers.'

'I'm Yadaka of the Guugu Yimithirr adopted Ngarigo.' He holds out his hand.

After a second Danny tentatively steps forward and shakes it. 'Danny.'

'I guess we're not strangers anymore.' Yadaka gestures for Danny to sit. He does. Beside Yadaka lie two long spear shafts, recently burnt to help straighten them. Another shorter, thicker stick is fashioned into another weapon or utensil of some sort. Yadaka prepared these when he was waiting for the right time to approach Molly, or her shanty, to look for food. He watched for two days. The smell of the meat aroma had led him to her place, but the arrival of the Clintoffs kept him at bay.

Yadaka pours the tea. Danny is intrigued by the black man – this is the closest he's ever come to one, as they're rare these days around these parts. The boy's eyes wander over every part of him.

He's not quite the giant Danny first thought. He's about six foot. Fit, but injured. The infected wound on his lower back is starting to heal nicely. The homemade ointment of moss and herbs seems to be working.

When Danny was about eight years old, he and his ma would see a tribe of blacks cutting through their property. His ma would say, 'They're goin' to do their dancin' and singin'.' When she was young herself, she and her da had stumbled upon a large gathering and been hunted away, screamed at in language. Molly had sensed straightaway that the blacks were doing something very important not meant for their eyes. The gathering was all men and young boys, painted in a powder of ground-down ochre rock mixed with water to make a paste and then applied to their bodies in different, distinct designs. She and her da took off and didn't look back. They kept running to put distance between the blacks and themselves. But later that night, on the wind, they could hear the tribesmen singing, chanting and stomping at the ground. In the days that followed it was the women they could hear, crying like a high-pitched howling wind.

These days the blacks keep their distance and Molly knows to keep hers, although a few times one older Aboriginal woman would hang back as the rest passed. She would stand some distance away, waiting and watching. Molly would present Joe Junior and Henry James, pushing Joe Junior forward, Henry James on her hip. The older woman would nod, then smile proudly, wave to Molly and head off to follow the others.

Puzzled, Danny would look at his ma, then back at the older black woman scampering away. Molly told him it was because that woman had helped at the births of his younger brothers. 'She was just checkin' on 'em – her babies too, in a way,' Molly would say, watching the older woman going on her way. There was a yearning in Molly's eyes, maybe for company. Maybe she missed this older gin. Maybe she thought, *This is what it's like to have a mother's care and concern for you.* Even though that care and concern came from afar. Molly only knew the woman as the kind gin who was there occasionally when she needed help. There was her da's death and three of Molly's six births – Baby Jack, Joe Junior and Henry James. And out of Molly's four miscarriages over the years before Danny finally arrived, the gin was there for one. Molly was in a very dangerous way after the loss and the woman nursed her back to good health. Then, like always, she'd clench her fist, blow through it, mumble something in language and was gone . . . How Molly did miss her care.

Danny drinks his tea. There is quiet between him and Yadaka as they sip their hot brew and ponder. Danny looks down and begins to finger the sharp wooden tips on the spear shafts that lie beside him.

'For huntin'. For food,' Yadaka informs him.

Danny's hand moves to the next spear. It has a sharp, jagged-edge bone tip. This was the bone Yadaka slipped into his pocket after his meal when he first arrived. He has shaped it into a dangerous-looking tip for the spear, making a ferocious weapon.

'Killin' spear, that one,' Yadaka says, as if reading Danny's mind.

Danny looks straight at the black man. 'Are you a bad man, then?'

'I don't think I am.'

Danny becomes a little afraid.

Yadaka stares off towards the thicket, letting Danny calm his nerves or giving him a chance to get up and run. Danny decides to stay. Yadaka sees this and appreciates the boy's trust in him. Still looking away, he says, 'Danny, I hope you never have to kill for any other reason than to eat.'

Danny turns away quickly. If Yadaka had been watching, he might have caught the flicker of guilt in Danny's eyes.

They drink and sit in silence for a little longer. An easiness and trust is quickly forming between the boy and man. Danny loves to talk, and if there is someone willing to listen, well, he can't help himself. 'I've not long had a birthday. Three months back now.'

'Really. Many happy returns to you. How old are you, Danny, if you don't mind me asking?'

'I'm twelve, sir.' A big smile creeps across Danny's lips, like the age has great meaning for him. 'My da was off workin' by this age, he reckons.'

'Is that what you're hoping for?'

'Not really. My ma needs help around the house. I'm a great help, she reckons. With Da bein' away a lot.'

Molly can't afford gifts for birthdays but always tries to make a special meal and have all the family there, especially if their da hasn't left for the drove yet. It's very rare he's home for any of the family's birthdays, so having Joe home on Danny's twelfth birthday, Molly wanted to make it special for her eldest son. She believed turning twelve was important: 'you are no longer a child, but not yet an adult'. You're at the crossroad, leaving your childhood before stepping up into adulthood. Danny could very well be off working, droving with his da and gone from Molly's life, lost to the goings-on in the world of work.

'You're ready for men's business,' Yadaka says, after a sip of hot tea.

'Is that the same men's business my da does with the whore woman to the west?'

Yadaka is surprised at Danny's casual remark, the boy clearly not understanding the 'whore' word.

'That's what Ma calls her. I think that's her last name.'

Yadaka can't help but grin. 'Well, this men's business is different to your da's men's business, but one day you'll be interested in that men's business too.' Yadaka has a little chuckle to himself. It's been a while for him too, regarding 'that' men's business.

The boy is eager to hear more about Yadaka's men's business, and Yadaka is keen to oblige with conversation. He can't help but enjoy the boy's company and his genuine interest in the black man's beliefs.

Yadaka tells Danny that he is halfway there. 'Your responsibilities to your ma, brothers and sister are one part. Then there is your responsibility to your jobs around the house.'

Danny nods, listening and taking it all in.

'But most importantly of all, there are stories of the land, the sky and the animals that you are to learn, and it's your responsibility to retell them to your sons. You learn this over time but the beginnin's are when you walk the mountain to the sacred spot.' Yadaka takes another sip of tea, whether he needs the drink or is creating a pause for dramatic effect. 'The final task will be your first kill, proper way.'

Danny's eyes widen, either with disbelief or fear. *First kill?*

Yadaka seizes the moment, gathering up a spear swiftly and demonstrating a fast, impressive killing action. 'To kill swiftly, no suffering.'

The boy closes his eyes tight like he is ridding himself of a horrible thought. Yadaka wonders if he has gone too far, and his menacing stance and facade fall away. He watches the boy for a second, then says, 'Danny, I was talkin' about your first kill bein' an animal. For food.'

Danny opens his eyes, relieved. Embarrassed, he looks at the ground. He sees Yadaka's bare feet – a welcome change of subject. Without missing a beat, he says, 'No boots? Did ya lose them?'

'No. Where's yours?'

'Got none. What do ya do when the snow falls?'

Yadaka can't help but smile; the boy is quick. 'You ask a lot of questions.'

'Ma says that, too. But if ya don't ask ya don't know, eh?'

'You answer all the questions you're asked?'

'Yes, sir. I like talkin'.' And off Danny goes, 'his yappin', his tongue waggin', his trap flappin',' as his ma would call it.

'Out here you don't get to do too much talkin'. Hardly any visitors – well, none. Only time I get to talk to anyone, other than my brothers or sister is when Ma sends me off to get food. Or maybe when the postman comes, but that's hardly ever and when he does he's always in a hurry. Ma has no family and neither does Da – well, none that he talks of. So for fun we make up stories to pass the day or night. The idea is to see how long ya can keep the yarn goin'. My ma's pretty good at spinnin' 'em,' he smiles, remembering her achievements.

'I tamed a bear in rough seas. Taught six horses to dance. Fed a tiger with my bare hands. And once was a clown called Tippo in a circus,' Yadaka says.

The boy bursts out laughing in disbelief. 'A tiger? A bear? Horses to dance?'

Yadaka can't resist his energy, 'It's true, every word.'

Danny brings his laughter under control, declaring his maturity. 'I'm twelve now, but that sounds like a pretty good yarn.'

Yadaka smiles admiringly at Danny. They sip their tea. Quiet and calm rests between them now. Yadaka brings the conversation back to the question Danny previously asked.

'So our feet don't get cold, when we see the first mist rise in the valleys, we come down from the mountain and head north for the winter.'

Danny considers this carefully. 'We've had the first mist – what are ya doin' still here?'

'Not for the want of tryin', let me tell you,' ponders Yadaka.

Another moment of silence passes between them. Yadaka continues: 'There are caves we use for our old or our sick who may not be able to make the journey. There are supplies. We come back then, in the spring.'

'But a decent man has boots. That's what my da reckons. A decent man has boots on his feet.'

'What does that make you and me then?' Yadaka replies. They both look at their dirty bare feet and share a smile.

'I'm supposed to be gettin' Da's boots this winter. I'll have to chock the heel though.' And it's Danny's turn to act out his story. He jumps up to demonstrate his da's badly bowed left leg. 'From when he was little,' he tells Yadaka, who watches and listens attentively. 'It had somethin' to do with his da, broke it and didn't get the leg fixed right. But we're too quick for him!' Danny does a sidestepping action to prove his point. 'He whipped his belt at me. Buckle end.' He rolls the top of his pants down to reveal a scar on his hip. Yadaka looks at him with empathy. The boy feels a little uncomfortable. 'Da didn't mean it – he was drunk. He does silly things.'

Danny quickly sits back down, uncomfortable and conscious of where this yarn could go. He'll get in trouble in more ways than one if his ma finds out. He's at it again, jabberin' and gasbaggin'. His hide will be skinned, pegged out to stretch, and tanned like the big wild grey bullock's out back. 'People don't need to know our business,' she always says.

But Danny can't help himself: he's never had this much attention bestowed upon him by a grown man who is genuinely taking an interest.

Yadaka throws the dregs of his tea away; he takes on the boy's discomfort and won't push this any further. But he knows what it means for this family: violence. Ginny May's voice comes back to haunt him: '... and a no-good man.'

'It's not what you wear on your feet, Danny, but how you carry yourself is what makes a decent man.'

Danny nods, agreeing. It's not certain that he genuinely understands, but he's content that Yadaka hasn't asked any further questions about his da and the belt. Danny's attention goes back to the spears – a conscious action to change the subject, perhaps, or just a child's nervousness in a predicament. He picks up the killing spear; it dwarfs him.

'Come. I'll show you,' Yadaka says, and with great athletic prowess throws the spear, burying its tip expertly into the ground many feet in front of them. Danny gratefully goes to retrieve it. Smiling and excited, he brings it back, happily leaping over debris that lies in his way like a playful puppy. Yadaka shows Danny how to hold and throw it. Danny's first attempt is an embarrassment but Yadaka is quick to encourage him. Danny eagerly tries again.

Unbeknown to Danny and Yadaka, Molly is watching from behind a tree. She is angered at first to see Danny defying her, but that subsides when she sees how much fun he is having. She watches Yadaka's fatherly encouragement and is impressed by how understanding and gentle he is towards her son. Strong and athletic, Yadaka again demonstrates for Danny how to throw the spear. His chiselled torso is something she hasn't witnessed before in a man. Molly catches herself admiring Yadaka's form and looks away, a little embarrassed, smiling to herself at her lingering thought.

She looks back and sees her son's little face light up with excitement, beaming from the attention. They mock-throw the spear a few times, then Danny throws it by himself. There is not a lot of power behind it, but his technique is on point. Yadaka places a gentle hand on the boy's shoulder, congratulating him. With love and pride, Danny looks up at his new-found friend. He runs off to retrieve the spear and lays it down next to the others. Then the two of them head off to the fallen tree. Each on one end of the saw, they begin to cut through the trunk. Danny is grinning from ear to ear.

Seeing this in her son brings Molly great joy and delight. She stands watching him proudly. Behind them, the sun begins to sink behind the mountain range. The night will soon be upon them.

NINETEEN

A spark flies into the air with a pop and crackle, the sap igniting from the ironbark logs, brought in especially for sale day. They line the main street of Everton. Small fires burn inside them. They're a slow and hot burn giving heat for the night and light and, every now and then, fireworks – bushman's way.

Thomas McNealy, the rogue swagman who was hunted from Molly's place by Yadaka, the brute who spoke so vividly of the Edwards murders, the sundowner who was quick to point the finger at the injured black on Molly's front lawn, saunters around the dark edges of the main street. People are still out mingling, eating, partaking in the festivities of the big sale day.

McNealy sidles up beside a group of high-society people studying the wanted posters of Yadaka that Trooper Leslie has dutifully plastered on shopfronts and posts along the main street. 'Heathen savage,' says one of the well-dressed gentlemen, his eyeglasses perched on the tip of his nose as he makes a closer inspection of the drawing.

'A dead black is a good black,' chides another.

'Not entirely true,' adds another. 'We had a good one. House Jacky. Docile soul. Trustworthy.'

His wife adds to the conversation: 'Surprisingly good worker.'

'Although not many of them are.' The gentleman steps away, removing his eyeglasses.

'Well, they look at us and think we do things the hard way.'

They all share the moment, chuckling among themselves.

'The detail of the drawing is very well done, one must say.'

They agree with one another.

A voice comes to them from the shadows: 'Seen him. Brute of a man.' McNealy steps into the light as a spark from an ironbark trunk flies into the air, sap popping. His timing is immaculate. The small crowd turns to him and he darts behind someone in the group, favouring their right side, his right hand animatedly helping to tell his tall tale.

'Big black fellow. Six-foot-six. No, six-foot-seven, easy.'

His beady little eyes flick from person to person, looking for anyone who has taken the bait. He darts behind someone else in the group. They follow his movements. 'Hungry, murderous eyes,' he whispers into one gentleman's ear as the sundower's left hand stealthily searches the gentleman's suit pockets.

The swaggie tips his hat and is on his way. 'Safe travels to your destination.'

McNealy has rattled them. They agree their safe return home is something they must consider if there is a murdering savage on the loose.

One of the gentlemen feels his side pocket. 'My chain watch! My gold pocket watch is gone!'

Rounding the corner of the Stanlow is Sergeant Clintoff. On seeing him, the gentleman's calls become more alarming: 'My watch! My gold pocket watch is gone! The bugger went that way. Rogue swaggie bastard!'

Hearing the outburst, Nate hurries off in the direction the gentleman points. He sees the culprit: a swaggie in a dirty, mismatched three-piece suit and soleless shoes, his feet kicking up high behind him as he runs full pelt down the platform that joins a few of the shopfronts together. Nate gives chase, favouring his injured leg, as the swaggie disappears behind one of the buildings.

When Nate reaches the building, McNealy is gone, lost in the large crowd milling around the entrance to the boxing tent. Drums beat a rhythmic *boomp-boomp, boomp-boomp* – the rhythm of a beating heart – calling wannabe fighters to their demise, lured into a bloodbath with the promise of money for a battle with the sideshow's best.

Inside, rowdy spectators line the worn canvas mat that marks the battleground. A single rope around the perimeter acts as a barrier and defines the boxing ring. On all fours, McNealy crawls through the crowd.

In the ring, Robert Parsen prances around warming up, bare-chested. John McPharlen fidgets around beside him. Their shirts and oilskin coats hang over the rope of their corner post. With his shirt off, McPharlen's physique is very much that of a boy. He sneers at the crowd, showing his rotten teeth.

Another stockman stands with them, his hat pulled low casting a shadow over his face. He holds a whiskey bottle up to their mouths and they each take a swig, their gloved hands necessitating his help. The two shirtless drovers step away to continue their limbering-up, rounding their shoulders, tossing their heads from side to side, pounding their gloves together as they watch their two opponents enter the ring. These are the sideshow boxers: Aboriginal men in shiny, colourful robes, all part of the performance.

'Tag-team boxing!' the ring announcer, who doubles as the referee, calls through his megaphone. The crowd roars its approval. The Aboriginal boxers remove their robes, showing their lithe upper bodies, and go through punching drills to showcase their skill, speed and ability.

'In the red corner we have Robert "The Red Bull" Parsen and John "The Joker" McPharlen, two stockmen back from the mountains looking to let off some steam!' The crowd roars, and hats fly into the air.

The announcer continues riling up the onlookers. Nate looks to the corner man and asks himself, *Is this Joe Johnson?* For Molly's sake he hopes it is, and that he'll be heading home soon.

'And in the blue corner, we have two of my best boxers – Lionel "The Killer" Kneebone and "The Destroyer", Digby Darling Downs.'

The crowd roars as the boxers flex their muscles, all part of the show. The bell sounds and Parsen and the bigger of the two Aboriginal boxers, 'The Destroyer', step into the middle of the ring. The other two step out, staying close to their respective corners. 'The Destroyer' raises his glove to tap in respect, but Parsen fakes and lands a punch straight into Digby's ribcage, breaking a floating rib. Digby takes a knee, but before the referee can step in, Parsen throws a loaded straight right that connects his opponent square on the jaw. Digby's head nearly spins off his shoulders. The boxer falls, knocked out before he even hits the canvas, and the referee signals that the fight is over.

The referee is frustrated his best boxer is injured and will be out for weeks, and the other Aboriginal boxer rushes in to help his mate. McPharlen throws himself at Parsen in celebration, and Parsen catches him in an embrace. Their corner man raises the whiskey bottle in triumph and drinks.

In the meantime, Nate has been scanning the crowd. He's just about to give up and head towards the man he thinks is Joe Johnson when he sees McNealy lifting the side of the tent to escape. Determined not to lose him again, Nate pushes his way through the boisterous crowd in McNealy's direction.

Back out on the main thoroughfare, Nate weaves his way through the crowd in the street, searching and investigating the darker corners of buildings. He reaches the Stanlow Inn and is about to go inside when the swing doors are thrust open and out spits the flying body of the rogue sundowner. He nearly collects Nate as he hurtles past, hitting the ground hard.

'You!' yells Nate, as he lunges after him.

But Nate stumbles, his bad leg giving way. McNealy rolls, springs to his feet and scampers off into the dark like a rodent.

Nate rubs at his leg, wincing with the pain, disappointed with himself and embarrassed – McNealy has made him look like a fool. A few onlookers come over to offer help but he waves them away. Grabbing for his hat, he slams it into his hand to dust off the mud. Dammit – he can only hope his show of skill with the two stockmen earlier in the day holds strong in the locals' minds.

TWENTY

Sitting by the fire pit, Molly mends a hole in her husband's old wool vest. She sings softly to herself as she sews: 'The purest smile and the gentlest of hands . . .' She looks tired, sombre. She holds up the vest, inspecting her work.

Danny sits close by watching Yadaka working on a bone, shaping it. He thinks, *Perhaps it's for another killing spear.* Yadaka files the bone against a rock, working one end to a sharp point.

Molly's soft, husky, gentle singing mixed with nature's night chorus makes for the perfect soundtrack to this moment that Danny is cherishing. His mother's singing is soothing and he has the male company of someone who wants to sit and be in the moment with him. With them.

'I love the ground on where she stands. Black, black, black is the colour of my true love's hair.' Molly's singing ends. She's caught up in the study of her handiwork when Danny's enthusiastic clapping breaks her concentration.

'Love it when ya sing, Ma.' Danny beams at her.

'Ya havin' a lend,' she says, blushing.

'Fine singer, missus,' Yadaka says, looking up from sharpening the bone. He is genuine and gives her a small smile of appreciation.

Molly is taken aback. *A compliment?* She doesn't know how to respond. *Praise?* And his smile, those perfect teeth. She quickly pulls at a thread that needs no attention and changes the subject, giving the focus to her son. 'Ya grandey's favourite, eh Danny?'

Danny happily shares the story: 'Sang it while he worked, sang it when he ate—'

Molly cuts in: 'Sang it in his sleep. Speakin' of – bed.'

Danny gives a little whine of protest but Molly is quick to inform him of his duties. 'Ya gotta be up at sparrow's fart to collect ya brothers and sister from the McGuinnesses'.'

Danny looks at his mum, a little perplexed. 'I was hopin' to help Yadaka finish the woodchoppin'.'

Molly shoots him a stern look. He knows what this means, and knows better than to argue. He heads inside to bed but stops short of the door and turns back. He's got an idea to stall his bedtime, perhaps. 'A story. Please, Ma.' He doesn't give his mother time to answer. 'Please? The bullock one.' Skipping back towards her: 'Yadaka might want to hear it.'

Daringly, he stands, hopeful, in front of her. 'No, wait – Yadaka, ya tell your story about the clown called Tippo! In the circus!'

Molly looks at Yadaka dubiously. Yadaka's not sure if he's brave enough to tell his story at this time. This woman means business when she pulls her faces. But Yadaka likes this family. A warmth grows in him in their presence, a warmth he hasn't felt since meeting and falling deeply in love with the Walgalu woman who became his wife. He likes spending time with Molly when she allows it. He takes his chance.

'Fillis Circus, missus. South African circus. I was good with the children who came to watch. Calmed a bear in rough seas. Toured the east coast, started up north in my home country of the Guugu Yimithirr, land of coloured sands and rainforest. They left me then, in Melbourne ... I was arrested for being destitute.'

Yadaka pauses as he swallows the emotion caught in his throat. That was a harrowing time. So young. Lost. And no one cared, because he was black. And he was just a boy.

'How old were you?' she asks.

'Same age as your Danny here.'

Molly is devastated. She couldn't fathom her son dealing with something like that. She sees the man's pain and feels for him. *How could anyone treat a child like that?*

Yadaka is surprised by his own emotional reaction to the story. He hasn't felt like this in years. Danny, so young and naive, sits eagerly waiting for the story to continue.

'Father Matthews got me out of jail. He gave me a white name, but I don't use it. Taught me to read, write and play the tuba.'

Molly can't believe what she is hearing. 'The tuba?' she asks, raising her eyebrows.

Yadaka nods and smiles. Molly smiles back. She catches herself and quickly busies herself with the vest again, the same piece of thread that needed no attention in the first place. Danny sees this as an opportunity and jumps in with his own story.

'About ten days back now – see, I was writin' in the dirt.' With his finger, Danny traces through the dirt in front of him, demonstrating his action. 'And Ma went to put the broom away when she heard this snortin' and gruntin'. The others were out back playin'.'

Danny rises, doing his mother's actions of listening. 'Ma goes to the door and cracks it open – and there is a big, wild, grey bullock! Horns the width of a grown man's arm span.' He spreads his arms as wide as he can and pushes his chest forward to gain more width, then stretches his fingers as far as they can go, willing them to reach beyond their capacity.

Yadaka jumps up and begins to mimic the bullock in the form of an Aboriginal dance. It's ancient tradition and something he is very good at. Molly jumps at his sudden movement. But Danny is excited by the interaction. He continues on with invested energy now that Yadaka is participating.

'Now my brothers and sister start to move around front, and the bullock looks over at 'em and stomps his hoof.' Yadaka follows Danny's story perfectly, flicking up the dirt with his feet. Molly jumps again at the sudden movement, her nerves shot. She feels a little foolish. Danny continues his impersonations of himself and his mother.

'I hand Ma the gun. She uses the doorframe as her guide, keepin' herself steady. The bullock lunges at my brothers and sister.'

Yadaka lunges and Danny squeals with delight. Molly jumps, squeezes her eyes closed.

'Bang! Shot him straight between the eyes!'

'What?' Molly stammers, as her eyes spring open in bewilderment, her breathing shallow. Yadaka and Danny both stare at her. She's become very flustered.

Demanding now, but still rattled, she says, 'Wh— what did ya just say?'

Danny is a little perplexed at his mother's reaction. 'How ya shot the bullock straight between the eyes.'

Molly draws in her breath, then sighs deeply with relief. She is silenced by her own reaction and foolishness.

Yadaka draws in closely, frowning with curiosity. He senses her anxiety and thinks, *There is something not right here.* He offers, 'We'll finish this story another night, Danny.' He feels maybe he should talk to Molly privately, ask if she needs any help. Her reaction is too extreme to ignore.

Danny is reluctant but does as he's told. He kisses his ma goodnight, shakes Yadaka's hand, gives a little nod of appreciation and disappears into the dark of the shanty.

The sounds of the night seem amplified to Molly. She rubs at her temples; she must hide the rush of emotion that is threatening to tip tears from her eyes. Her shoulders slightly lurch and a dry-retching sound escapes her pursed lips. She's going to vomit! She quickly clamps a hand over her mouth and manages to hold the flood back.

This is not about what I thought I heard Danny say. It's all been too much. I gave birth only yesterday, and I'm weak. Only this mornin' I buried my baby girl, after all – another child I'll never hold again, never see grow. And I'm yearnin' for the others – Joe Junior, Henry James and little Delphi. I miss them too much, and I worry for them. I've had a bloody wild bullock land on my doorstep, unexpected English vistors sniffin' around and the old bastard swaggie – it's no wonder I never feel safe in my own home. And now I'm harbourin' a runaway black man, for goodness sake! I'm emotional and physically drained – of course I'm hearin' things. I'm tired, my mind's playin' tricks on me. Of course!

Trying to take hold and calm herself down, she sighs again deeply and dabs at the tears that have finally spilt from her eyes.

Full of a tenderness Molly's not used to, Yadaka asks, 'You right, missus?'

Molly closes her eyes. She's not sure what to say, or if she should say anything. He's a black and has no right to ask her questions: how dare he? 'The last few days catchin' up on me.'

She goes and grabs her broom and starts her routine of sweeping the loose top layer of dirt, starting out the front, working her way back, getting rid of the day's foot traffic. Evidence.

Caught in the awkwardness that lies between them now, Yadaka watches her, wanting to reach her but not sure what to do, or what he *should* do. He opts not to push the subject – the last few days would be catching up on her, and fair enough. He removes the burning log from the fire, snuffing out its flaming end. Only the hot coals burn in the pit and they will eventually die down. He heads around the back.

As he makes his way to his sleep place, his mind races with wild thoughts and feelings. Why should he care so much about this woman's wellbeing? He knows he can't afford to invest any more in this family; he will soon be leaving. He must. Troopers will be swarming the area anytime now. In their eyes, he is a wanted man – for theft, and mass murder. But he can't help his fondness for the boy. He's a good boy. And he's become increasingly curious about the rest of the children – and about Molly. Watching her by the fire tonight, he noticed that its amber glow softened her. She seemed relaxed and content as she mended the old vest. He smiles as he remembers catching a sideward glance: the warm light of the flames highlighted the gold in her light-brown hair, and brought a glow to her skin. She looked . . . beautiful.

But he wonders why this little family is hiding out here in the middle of nowhere, so isolated. Is it for a reason? Especially after Molly's reaction tonight; she was possessed with fear and pain, and Yadaka could feel it.

Molly watches from the front as Yadaka disappears into the darkness of the night. She knows she has revealed too much vulnerability and must watch herself tomorrow. She needs to be strong, needs him to be gone. She sweeps his tracks away, then suddenly a cold shiver runs over her. She spins, looking out into the dark surrounds of her front yard. With the fire low, it is hard to see. The moon is not quite full and is still to climb high in the night sky. She sees only the silver shimmer of snow gums, looking like dancing whimsical spirits, the branches reaching. Are her eyes playing tricks on her? Her eyes dart to the woodheap, the uneven ground very clear. A cold shiver runs over her again. She looks hard into the darkness beyond the woodheap, straining her eyes. Is there someone there, some thing?

She turns to go inside, and there behind her is the menacing silhouette of a man in a hat! Molly lets out a tight, muffled scream, not wanting to alarm her son who she hopes is asleep. In her haste to get away, she stumbles to the ground. The stranger walks towards her, his hand outstretched. Molly kicks out at him. She swings her broom, hoping to connect, fending off this beast. Her mind's eye flashes with images that blind her to her reality, spurring her on to fight. She rolls over to scamper away but the terror she feels paralyses her. She is caught in some moment in her mind, and the terror in her eyes is a clear and true indication. Finally, a familiar gentle voice breaks the horror: 'Missus, it's me!'

Molly snaps a look at the man behind her, and there stands Yadaka, the hat in his hands.

She's exasperated. 'What ... what are you doin' with that hat?' She tries to bring her breath and fear under control.

Yadaka is embarrassed and feels terrible for the fear he has put in her, the last thing this woman needed.

'I found it in the shed. Just inquiring if I could have it?' He feels stupid in asking, sounding like a little boy who has just found a toy. He offers his hand to help her up, but she ignores it.

Molly heaves herself up off the ground and dusts herself down.

She is very emotional and begins to tear up. Yadaka hangs his head to give her some privacy.

'No, you cannot. Give it here.'

Yadaka offers it to her and she snatches it away from him and heads inside, locking the door behind her.

Once inside, Molly can't contain her emotions any longer. She leans on the door, holding the latch for support, and breaks down crying, silently, her body lurching with spasms of emotion. She has clearly been bottling something up, needing to burst, and seeing Yadaka in the hat, silhouetted against the night, was the final straw. She weeps silently and openly. Behind her tough exterior are a heart and feelings.

Then, with all her might, she pulls herself together just as quickly as the emotion burst. Marching towards her kitchen stove, she throws the hat in and watches the flames engulf the felt.

Through the gaps in the shanty walls and by the light of the candle Danny lit to sleep by, Yadaka sees the bedroom curtain pulled for privacy. He is stumped. *What is going on with this woman, Missus Joe Johnson?* Yadaka is intrigued, and regretful his time will run out before he can get to the bottom of it. He's got to get that wood chopped and stacked and be gone, for his own safety – put mileage between here and where he is heading.

Frost sits on the grass of the alpine plain, an eerie mist hovering just above it. Nestled in the mist is Molly's shanty.

Out the back, wrapped in an old horse blanket, his back against the smokehouse, Yadaka sleeps soundly, despite the many thoughts that plagued him before his eyes finally closed. He needs to rest now – he will be on his own again soon, running from everything and everyone. The nights have turned cooler; winter has arrived. Suddenly he springs awake, jumping to his feet and sweeping up the killing spear that lies beside him, raising it high and poised, ready to defend himself.

Danny comes to an abrupt stop, his hands raised in surrender. 'Yadaka, it's me!' he whispers.

Curtly, Yadaka warns, 'Don't sneak up on a man like that, Danny. You could get yourself killed.'

Danny nods, looking very apologetic. Yadaka lowers the spear. A crow caws in the trees above, welcoming the new day; Yadaka turns to face it and nods, acknowledging. The first rays appear over the distant mountains to the east. A morning chill runs through both Yadaka and Danny, the temperature dropping with the rising of the sun.

Still wrapped in his horse blanket, Yadaka makes his way over to the fire pit and blows on the coals. Before long there are flames eating at the kindling. He positions some deadwood over the flames and the fire takes hold.

Awkwardly, Danny speaks. 'I'm headin' out now. I'll be back tomorrow afternoon. You can teach me to throw the spear and do my . . . men's business,' he adds, hopefully.

Yadaka looks up from warming his hands, wishing he could give more to this boy. 'I won't be here, Danny.'

Danny is devastated. 'You have to be!'

Yadaka, feeling sorry for Danny and smiling at him, indicates the smaller spear over where he slept; he can't deny he has grown very fond of the boy in this short time. 'You can have that one. You're a smart boy, you'll work out how to throw it. But never at your brothers.' This is Yadaka's attempt at lightening the moment.

Danny knows Yadaka must go. The logs have been cut and brought to the front of the house, ready to be split and stacked, and with the moon full tonight, he will be gone. Danny can't hide how he feels. He doesn't want Yadaka to go.

Wish I could tell him how I feel. That he means somethin' to me. More than my own da, if I'm honest. A friend to trust and to share my secrets with . . . ease my burden. And he'll know what to do. He'll make it right. And then Ma will be safe and Joe Junior and Henry James can play on the woodheap as much as they like. I haven't felt this safe at home in a long, long time. It'll be sad to have that feelin' go. And it will be gone when Yadaka leaves.

Yadaka sees Danny's little face distort with mixed thoughts and emotions. He places a hand gently on Danny's shoulder and gives it a little squeeze. 'I've enjoyed our time together, Danny. This was special for me. You're a good boy, young man. You look after your ma – she's a good woman. And remember what I taught you.'

Danny avoids looking up at Yadaka – his emotions are raw.

The moment is broken by the voice of Molly coming from the door of the shanty. She calls to her son. Danny turns to go but stops short, rubs at his nose with the back of his sleeve and sniffles, drawing up his snot. He's been trying desperately to hide his emotions. He turns back, throwing himself into a big hug with Yadaka.

Moved, the man receives the boy as if he were his own, holding him tight, patting him affectionately on the back and then pushing him towards his mother. But Danny resists. Bringing his hand up to shield his mouth, he whispers into Yadaka's ear. Bewildered, Yadaka pushes Danny back at arm's length.

From where Molly is watching, she's a little concerned. She sees Yadaka not understanding. He mouths the words, 'What did you say?'

Molly calls to Danny again, tersely this time. He hears his ma's tone and goes directly to her.

As Danny runs back to his mother, he considers what he just said to Yadaka and questions his judgement on sharing it. But if he's to go by the look on Yadaka's face, it's clear the black man has not understood what he said anyway. Or has he?

Mother and son head inside, Danny throwing a quick glance back to Yadaka, who stands looking baffled at what he's just heard and trying to make sense of it.

TWENTY-ONE

The Clintoffs' property is a quaint early-Victorian-style two-bedroom house. Formal in appearance, but plain. A pitched, hipped roof of shingles. A verandah out front and down one side that has been closed in, ornamentation restrained, an off-white picket fence the finishing touch. The property sits just off the main thoroughfare to Everton. The open-plain country makes the house easy to see, and access effortless. There is smoke rising from the chimney. A blanket of frost covers the front lawn.

Nate sits on the side of the bed looking pretty worn down – last night was rough and long. Bruises are forming on his upper body from the fights and scraps he's had over the last twenty-four hours.

After he lost out to the thieving swagman, he went toe to toe, hit for hit with a few drunken stockmen. He was incredibly grateful for their inebriated state. Then he walked the slight incline to the jailhouse so many times he lost count, with more drunk stockmen – and a few gentlemen too. It was a huge effort to get them up the hill and hurl them into the cells. This morning he feels every strained muscle he used in surviving yesterday's mayhem and lawlessness.

He struggles to put on his boots. He hears Louisa in the kitchen clanging pots and pans as she prepares breakfast. She sneezes. Nate calls to her, 'Bless you.'

'Thank you.'

'You should see a doctor. You don't feel any better, Louisa?'

'I'm fine,' she says, just as a huge coughing and sneezing fit comes on.

'Louisa?'

'Oh, dear me.' She sniffles and wipes at her nose. 'Seriously, I'm fine. I'm more concerned for Missus Johnson, and wonder about her birth and what she's had. New baby – wouldn't it be wonderful, Nate?'

Nate looks up to find her standing in the bedroom doorway.

'Nate?'

Finally, his boot slips on.

'A baby to goo and gah over?'

Nate strides over to Louisa and takes her in his loving arms, pressing her close to his bare chest. Louisa, loving his scent, breathes him in, nuzzling his neck and kissing the bruises on his chest and shoulders. His upper torso is defined by muscle: compensation for his lame leg. She places her hands gently on his chest, knowing how to get her way, and slowly moves them up around his neck, leading him to her lips. A gentle kiss, her glazed eyes connect with his.

'Do you really have to go in so early?'

'Why, Mrs Clintoff. Are you trying to seduce me with your son still asleep in his cot?' Nate looks back to little sleeping Samuel. 'That's a little unusual – he's normally up, running about causing chaos.'

'He had a restless night – his nose was a little blocked. But don't you go changing the subject! Call it what you want – I want a baby, Nate.'

She pulls his face to hers, devouring his mouth. He responds passionately, but after a few lustful moments pulls away and holds her at arm's length.

'Not now, sweetheart. I have to collate details and release twenty men this morning. I have to find a murderer and . . .' playfully, he continues on, '. . . how irresponsible of you to kiss me so lustfully with you having a cold!' He pats her on the bottom as he pushes past her to the kitchen table. 'My plate's still empty, woman,' he jokes.

Louisa can't help but smile at his playfulness. She knows she will pick up this moment again – this evening, perhaps? She watches Nate at the table, putting on his shirt. What a fine specimen of a man she has. After another fit of coughing, her voice strained now from the burning she feels in the back of her throat, she tells Nate she would love to go out and see Molly and the baby. 'How thoughtless of me – we should have offered to take her children back.' Louisa thinks it's a grand idea, smiling to herself as she turns her perfectly fried eggs. 'I hope she's okay out there.'

Nate considers it. It's not a bad thought. Louisa goes about preparing his plate. But he's hoping that Joe Johnson has had his fill of drinking, fighting and fucking and has headed home. Nate didn't lock him up last night with the two others from his team, so he's hoping he's already back with his family.

Louisa breaks her husband's thoughts: 'Any advancement in the murder case?' She places his plate of bacon and eggs in front of him.

With a resigned tone, he replies, 'We have troopers coming from the north and south – they should arrive in a day or two. Then we'll head back out to the Edwards property for a thorough search. But to be honest, I don't know where to begin.' He shakes out his napkin, places it across his lap and begins to eat.

Louisa returns to the sizzling bacon just as a stagecoach leaving Everton races past. The rattling of the undercarriage and the thundering hooves of the horses cause her to look up. She glances out the little window above her stove and there, on the main thoroughfare, she notices a shifty-looking swagman. Unbeknown to her, it's the same thieving sundowner her husband chased and lost last night, Thomas McNealy. He's heading out of town, a bottle of liquor under his arm, reciting, to himself something of grandeur and waving his hands. *Poor senile man*, Louisa thinks, but only for a second. A cold shiver runs through her.

Nate asks, 'Have you been all right here by yourself? I worry about you and Samuel.'

In the dust of the passing stagecoach the swagman shuffles along. Just before turning back to answer her husband, Louisa sees the sundowner leave the track and head into a small section of thick scrub not far from their home. Her breath catches in her throat.

'Yes, fine. Thank you.' She doesn't want to bother Nate: he has a lot to do already this morning. She surely doesn't need to worry about a harmless old swagman having a tipple in the peace and quiet of the scrub.

'Thank you for this.' Nate slops a piece of bacon in the runny yolk of his egg. 'Just what I needed. I don't think I ate much yesterday. Can you fix Trooper Leslie a plate? He's been there all night.' Louisa is happy for the distraction and glad to help. She grabs another plate and fills it.

'Can you come home for lunch today?' she asks, looking towards the scrub where the swagman disappeared.

Nate immediately looks up, egg falling from his fork, concern clear on his face. 'Of course.'

Louisa hears his concern. 'Samuel would love to spend some time with his papa.'

'What time?' Nate goes back to eating.

Louisa does the maths as she wraps up the breakfast for Trooper Leslie. 'Say, one o'clock?'

'One it is.' Nate pushes his empty plate away.

'Before you go, I need to show you something.' She skips past him, coughing as she goes to her work desk in the far corner of the living room.

'Is this another attempt at stalling me?' he teasingly asks.

On the desk sits a mimeograph and wax paper, the departing gift from her father. Beside it is a stack of printed papers. She grabs one from the pile and presents it to Nate.

'Well, well, well.' He looks over the paper. 'So proud of you, sweetheart.'

Pleased with herself, Louisa smiles, sniffling into her handkerchief. 'First published female writer of Everton. Which, by the way, is named after Evelyn Edwards. How's that for local trivia?' she manages, proudly standing before her husband like a schoolgirl handing in an assignment.

He smiles affectionately at her, and says, 'Founding family. Arriving 1820s. Top that.'

Louisa takes a seat on his lap, draping her arms around his neck. 'Folklore has it that Charles Edwards fathered a black child. The whitest ... whitest something around.'

Dubiously, Nate looks at his wife questioningly.

'What?' she asks, sheepishly.

Raising an eyebrow, he says, 'May one ask, how did you come by this information, and under what guise did this conversation take place?'

Nonchalantly, with a nervous cheeky grin, she says, 'Miss Shirley called it history.'

A deep sexy chuckle escapes Nate and he goes back to peruse the paper, then reads from it: '*Battered wives: is it purely a husband's right?* Serious topic to introduce yourself with.'

Louisa stiffens on Nate's lap, saying, 'My sister remained silent and met her death, Nate. City life, bush or mountain country, we must give the subject of violence towards women a voice. It needs to be legislated.'

He gently takes her beautiful face in his hands, entirely in love with her, in awe of her and grateful for her strength and determination. Nate kisses his wife deeply, and she passionately submits, feeling safe and loved in his strong arms that wrap tightly around her, and he in hers.

A plate of partially eaten bacon and eggs sits to one side of the desk as Trooper Leslie scribbles frantically with his dip pen on a piece of paper. It reads: *ARREST: DRUNK AND DISORDERLY*. On his other side, a pile of arrest papers mounts. The jail was absolutely at capacity the previous night.

Robert Parsen, the stockman from the boxing-tent fight, the stockman Nate kept a close eye on due to his connection with Joe Johnson, approaches the trooper's desk. He indicates the stack of arrest papers and says, 'This is a first.'

John McPharlen, his boy sidekick, pulls at a loose rotten tooth and joins him. He hands Parsen his oilskin. These two are regulars in the lock-up at sale time. There is something in their eyes that can't be trusted. *If they weren't hardworking stockmen, they would more than likely be ruthless outlaws*, Nate thinks. It's what Spencer Leslie said when they were locking them up last night. They were so drunk that they couldn't have hurt anyone, but spinning the barrel of a gun and holding it to your head to prove loyalty wasn't the best idea to show their comradeship. Locking them up was for their own safety.

Nate stands at the utility cupboard getting their pistols and shotgun. He removes their nametags from the weapons and hands them back. Nate answers Parsen's question: 'Just a precaution. Need to record offenders. A way to track crime. Suspects.'

McPharlen leans into Nate's face, far too close, his breath revolting. 'The fuckin' murderer is one of those fuckin' savage black niggers. No decent fuckin' white man could murder an upstandin' white woman and her children.'

Nate doesn't flinch, although his stomach turns from the stench of McPharlen's breath. 'Thank you for your opinion, Mister McPharlen. Duly noted.' Nate steps away to the other side of the desk.

Parsen has filled in the forms with 'No Fixed Address' on both. Nate studies them as McPharlen signs his name with an 'X'. *He's left-handed.* Nate notes. 'Joe Johnson head home?' Nate casually asks.

The stockmen look at each other, dumbfounded. 'Was he in town?' asks Parsen.

'His horse was in the yard. I'm assuming—'

Parsen cuts in. 'No, we found his horse runnin' with some brumbies. We're headin' out there later today. See if our old mate's all right. First time in eight years he's missed the drove.'

Nate is perplexed. This revelation completely contradicts what Molly said. He continues with his questioning. 'You sit up in the mountains with the sheep for ... what? Three months?' Parsen and McPharlen nod. 'And Joe Johnson was not with you?'

They both nod again. Cocky McPharlen can't help himself: 'First time in eight years. Ya hear him, yeah?' Nate's beginning to dislike this man-boy.

The two stockmen leave. Spencer has watched the exchange and sees the quizzical look on Nate's face. 'Sir?'

'That just contradicts everything she said.'

'Beg your pardon, sir?'

Nate contemplates, remembering Molly's words: 'My Joe's a drover. Been away three months now. My Joe brings all the supplies home.'

Then Nate remembers hearing her talking to her eldest son about bringing supplies home – she gave him a list. *What is going on? Why would she lie about her husband's whereabouts?* Nate's concern has shifted slightly. He's still worried for Molly's safety, and the safety of her brood – there is still a murderer on the loose in the district, after all – but what he has just discovered has triggered something else in him. Maybe he does have to get out to the Johnson property, because maybe 'her Joe' isn't coming home. Maybe he upped and left her. She will need protection, a woman on her own, with children, in the high country. Baffled, Nate sighs in exasperation as he considers all of this.

'Sir?' inquires Spencer again. 'Who contradicted themselves?'

'Molly Johnson.'

TWENTY-TWO

Molly wipes the sweat from her brow and places a hand on her lower back as she stands upright and stretches out. Under the front awning of her verandah, the new woodpile is almost complete. She stacks the heap while Yadaka splits the logs. Only a few remain. His work here is almost done.

Yadaka brings down the sharp axe and splits a piece of wood in two. He throws them gently at Molly's feet and she bends to scoop them up and pile them on the woodheap. Yadaka takes her in as he works, this hardworking, healthy, handsome, nurturing woman. He can't help but admire her. He's only been staying at her property a short time, but there is something about Missus Joe Johnson that has him genuinely intrigued.

Yadaka says, 'This big wind picked up ...' – Molly looks at him, taking in her surroundings as if looking for the wind – '... all around but never touching me.' She realises it's the beginnings of a story and gives her attention to him. She enjoys a yarn, and appreciates the pause in the backbreaking job at hand.

'Straight up.' He moves his hands, mimicking a whirlwind. 'No good, see. Ran all the way home then. That's when I found them – my woman – dead. She was beautiful.' Yadaka gets caught in the memory and stops what he is doing to fully appreciate his vision of his wife. 'Black shining skin in the full moonlight ...' It's as if she stands before him. Maybe in his mind's eye she does?

Molly is taken aback by the openness and beauty of Yadaka's speech and, maybe, him for the first time. This gentle, kind, caring, handsome ... man. Molly becomes awkward, feeling as if she is intruding on a private personal moment.

'... and when she danced, smooth like shallow running water over river rocks ...'

Molly clears her throat, slightly uncomfortable with the intimacy of what he's just shared. Yadaka is a little embarrassed to have revealed so much of himself. He hasn't felt safe, ever, to share that story with anyone, until now. Maybe he should tell her? All of it, everything. Yet what good would it do? He's leaving tonight, going home. But what's there? He's been away for almost twenty-three years, and if the development in the north is anything like the development in the south, does he even have a home or family or a way of life to go to?

Molly sees his concern and he turns to her, saying, 'I found my wife and my children, all the old people ... dead. Slaughtered.' A moment of silence passes. 'Reading the tracks left behind, I could tell my family were forced into the river, the water slowing them ...' Emotion catches in his throat. 'They were fired upon from both banks ... an ambush. Calculated and planned. Murder.'

Molly nods in acknowledgement. She knows of the brutality and callous law towards the blacks, and has no words.

Yadaka shakes the memory from his mind. They look at each other again, and for the first time they connect on another level, sharing in the grief of losing loved ones. Children. Molly is deeply touched and finally manages to say, 'I'm so sorry to hear of your loss.'

Yadaka manages a little nod of appreciation. He can't look at her, deeply moved by her sincere reaction to his pain. He busies himself with the task at hand.

Yadaka grabs another log and splits it in half. But he can't help but continue: this releasing of his story feels right. 'The tribe put me out. I wouldn't go with them for payback.' He splits one half again. Molly sees his hurt. No amount of time could ever heal such a trauma. 'I knew nothing would come of it. Too many whites, too many guns now.'

He splits the other half and tosses the four pieces at Molly's feet. Only the sound of nature and the caw of a distant crow can be heard, filling the silence between them. Yadaka turns in the direction of the caw and pays his respects with a nod.

'Why do you do that?'

'What?'

'Acknowledge the caw of the crow.'

'It's my mother's mother's mother's totem, and the carrier of souls to the Dreaming. The crow also has a special place in my clan's creation story.'

Molly is intrigued.

'I'm just paying my respect, either way,' Yadaka adds.

'Thanks for sharin' that.' Molly says, as she gathers up the pieces of wood and goes back to her stacking. Time to put her emotions in line.

I'd have to be made of the river rock not to be moved by his story. To lose ya wife, that's one thing – but ya whole family? Three babies? At the hands of callous men in their charge for progress? I shake my head at the vision conjured there. I've seen this aggression with my own eyes … Ya could only have pure hate to be driven to such an act, surely. But I heard my da talkin' about the encounters with the braggin' men of entitlement who rained down terror on those blacks. Ha, when

I think back now, once the whiskey was finished, the fights my da got into were with those very same men. Maybe that explains his soft spot for the Aboriginal woman who sometimes visited.

I would have put myself in front of one of those murderous bullets that decimated his family ... To witness such a thing? I wouldn't have had the strength to continue. His resilience is to be honoured. I wonder if this is what happened to the gin who helped with my da in his death, and the birth of my three sons – it's been a long time since I saw her.

Molly turns back to see Yadaka standing at the water barrel. He drinks. He removes his shirt, dips a rag into the wash bucket and freshens himself up, wiping his face then his chest ... *And for some godforsaken reason I'm drawn to this man.* Molly's breath catches – she has never felt this way before. New feelings – tingling sensations – ripple through her body, in parts she has never felt, and she feels shock *and pleasure* that you could get these sort of sensations there. She bites down hard on the inside of her mouth to snap out of whatever this ridiculousness is. She is desperately trying to find some common sense in all of these overwhelming feelings.

There's not so much different between us, perhaps. Grief, we share. Loss, and grief. Love for our kin. His care and concern, his gentle way through the delivery of my stillborn baby girl – it all makes sense now. He ain't no heathen savage, that much I know. If any of them are.

Dammit, this is what happens when ya let people in. I can't show weakness, can't let anyone in. Got too much at stake.

He senses Molly behind him, watching. 'I'm headin' home. Followin' the eastern highlands runnin' north to my mother's country,' Yadaka says, finally breaking the silence.

Molly knows she can't get caught up in his life story. Her hard exterior returns, for her own sake more than his. 'Why ya tellin' me this?'

'A life's story untold is a life not lived, missus.'

Molly thinks on this a moment – he's right, and her da would have thought the same.

He looks at her suggestively, hoping she might open up and share more of her story with him. But Molly knows she must hold strong, and her sternness quickly returns.

'Ya mentioned ya headin' home – well, I'm not stoppin' ya.' She doesn't want to sound too rude, but she needs him to know she's not interested. She will not allow herself to be. The help he has offered is all she wants or needs from this man – this black man.

Yadaka pauses and looks at her as she goes about straightening the already perfectly stacked woodheap. He understands, but the silence is getting the better of them and they both know it. Yadaka decides to break it before he loses her to the inside of the hut. Putting his shirt back on, he grabs the ladle and pours a scoop of water into a tin cup, taking it to Molly.

'I saw the stone in your burial grounds marked Mary. That your mother's grave?' Molly jumps on hearing him so close behind her. She quickly turns, but can't hide her flushed cheeks. She takes the water and drinks, praying the cool water will take the heat from her face. But in her mind's eye all she sees is Yadaka, this morning bringing the water up from the Murrumbidgee, his muscles straining under the weight of the full buckets on his fourth and final trip to fill the barrel. She felt privileged this morning, as that was her job normally. And the sight of him was pretty spectacular if she dare think on it. *Oh, my goodness! Stop this foolishness, woman!*

'Sorry, what did you ask?' He can't help but smile, and *dammit, those perfect teeth*.

'The rock in your burial grounds?'

'Oh, yes, no, somethin' I just did. That's all my da told me about her. My ma. Her name. Mary. Chipped it in there myself.'

Molly steps away. Feeling very awkward now, she chides herself again at her behaviour and the ridiculous thoughts and feelings that are rushing through her. Was this what Miss Shirley warned her about when she had her first bleed and went to stay with her to learn of 'women's ways'? *Oh dear, I couldn't imagine Miss Shirley feelin' anything like this!* Molly's own husband never sparked these feelings she's experiencing, let alone ask about the rock – Mary's rock – and he was the one who placed it in the family graveyard for her.

Molly finishes the water, putting the cup back at the barrel, and clears her throat. 'Molly, pet name to Mary.' As soon as she has said the words, she wishes she could take them back.

Yadaka catches his breath, shocked she's offered this piece of personal information. Choking on the inhalation, he coughs in amazement – she's told him something personal. *Her name.* Has he finally won her trust?

Guli-gulaba! Yes, all right, this is good. No white woman has ever given me her first name. I know never to ask for it, or to use it. And what a beautiful name it is: Molly.

Never thought I would feel *this* again, not after the death of my wife – and with a white woman? But there is somethin' about this woman, Molly. I just can't put my finger on it. Or is it more that I am so desperate and damaged, and looking to see more than what is really happening here? I hope I don't show it. But I find Molly's strength, courage, determination and the love for her children so appealing, and cannot help ... these deep urges ... Is it out of convenience for us both that these feelings are surfacing or is this really happening? I wonder if she feels it too.

Not wanting the moment to end, Yadaka starts to ask another question, but Molly cuts him off. Indicating the now-finished, stacked woodheap, sitting perfectly under the awning of her verandah for easy access and out of the elements, she says, 'Thank you. Time to go.'

No! No! NO! Thoughts race through Yadaka's mind. *No, we have just begun. Stall! Think, dammit, think!* 'Can I clean up, eat and leave at dusk, missus?'

'That's your business. Just stay away from the house. You're done here.' With that, she straightens up and heads inside.

Yadaka has to think fast to hold her attention. All he could come up with is, 'Thank you, missus.'

She turns back to him, and finally they lock eyes. She nods her appreciation. 'Travel safe,' she says, and she means it. She heads inside, closing the front door behind her.

Yadaka hears the lock latching. He stands there, unable to hide his disappointment. He can't help but wonder, *What if ... ?* He knows he must leave: it's for all their safety. There is nothing here with this white woman and her four white children, not in their lifetime, anyway. Even though he knows of a story of forbidden love between a black and a white. It was frowned upon on both sides. Life is hard enough.

TWENTY-THREE

At the other end of Everton, on the highest rise in the town, a modest-sized stone cottage and church sit side-by-side on a decent parcel of land. It is the McGuinness residence. An elderly Aboriginal man tends to the rose bushes that sit between the house and the church. He takes his time turning the soil at the base of each bush.

Sergeant Clintoff walks past and the old Aborigine struggles to get up off the ground to appropriately address the man of authority in his presence. He finally manages to stand and nods respectfully, turning it into a formal bow. Nate smiles at the old man, uncomfortable with the formality of it all. The Aboriginal man lowers himself carefully back down, turning the soil methodically, his mind elsewhere as he smiles to himself.

Tethered out the back is Danny's new purchase, the horse his ma instructed him to buy. Nate is impressed – Danny has a good eye. The mare is off-white with a caramel-coloured mane and tail and big chocolate-drop eyes. She would have been a pretty little filly.

Nate joins Danny, who is brushing her down. 'Sorry to hear about your little baby sister. Miss Shirley just told me.'

Danny continues without looking up. 'Death's a part of life, sir. It happens.'

Nate notes Danny's maturity. Indicating the horse, he says, 'You think you'll get foals out of her?'

'Doubt it. She's too old. The man who sold her said her time for breeding is done. But she's strong, and we'll get some good years out of her yet.'

'Your da home yet, Danny?' The question jars Danny; he looks up at Nate but then quickly busies himself again brushing the horse, walking around to the other side to avoid the question.

Nate pushes further: 'Sale's done now. He'd have the supplies, so I guess he'll be heading home then?'

Danny stops what he is doing and, peering over the back of his horse, looks Nate straight in the eye. 'Yes, sir.'

Nate tries to see through the boy. Is he hiding something? Does he know anything? Nate strokes the bridge of the horse's nose and brings the conversation back to the animal that stands between them. He asks a few more questions. Its name? How many hands tall is it? What was the trade on it? Danny accommodates his questions but never once looks at Nate.

Danny continues brushing. Once finished, he checks the hooves for damage – they may need repairing. The poor animal will have to carry four children home tomorrow, a four-hour trip with a heavy load. It's one of the reasons Danny got her: she was a packhorse, and used to carrying weight over long distances. 'A big heart,' the previous owner said.

Danny works away patiently, detangling her tail. 'You've done a fine job, Danny.'

'It's part of my chores at home. I groom and tend to Da's horse before he leaves and after he comes back from a drove.'

Nate thinks back to the state of Joe's mare that was left in the holding yard at the sale. She was in a very poor way and looked a lot worse for wear than the other working horses. Even though they are out on country working, a stockman will always brush down his horse once he finishes for the day.

Nate has a few more questions about Danny's da now that the boy seems to be comfortable with their conversation. He asks, 'Did you see your da leave for the drove, Danny?'

Still not looking at Nate, Danny's focus is on the last blasted knot of hair as he says, 'No, sir.'

Nate straightens up, alert to the fact he might be onto something. Danny has seen this and pauses for dramatic effect. He's not silly: he knows what the sergeant is doing. 'Long gone before we're up,' Danny adds with a half-cocked eyebrow.

Nate sees it and fires another question at him: 'Your da ever been late to come home?'

Danny gives one more final look over the horse, his ego leading the way now, thinking he's outsmarted the big-city sergeant. 'Sometimes he goes straight on to another drove or out to this place—' Danny stops himself, but it's too late. He's flapping his trap again. Suddenly anxious, he pretends to find something on the horse's hind leg.

Nate knows he's got him. The boy does know something. Nate pushes a little more: 'Where's this place?'

Danny focuses on the mark on the horse's back leg, picking at it. 'Danny? You ever been there?'

Danny knows he's said too much and there's no way of turning his words around. Guilt is written all over his face as he says, 'Please don't tell Ma. It was only the once.'

The sun's high in the sky, not a cloud in sight on the wide-open plains. At a crossroads, a dirt cloud rises from the track as a rider and horse belt along it. The horse soon comes to an abrupt stop, smack bang in the middle of the junction.

It's Nate. He looks at his pocket watch: it's nearly one o'clock, and his lunch-date promise to his wife weighs heavy on his mind. He looks off into the distance and sees their home, smoke streaming steadily from the chimney, knowing she will have cooked something special and his little boy will be anxiously awaiting his arrival.

Nate's gut instinct has never let him down; it's how he survived the war with only a wound to his leg. In battle under heavy fire, he went back in to retrieve a fellow soldier. He hid himself behind a small shrub, weighing up his options. He was about to run in through the front door of a deserted building but instinct told him to go around the back. And there he found his mate, heavily wounded. As he was dragging him to safety, Nate was shot by a sniper. He was lucky to escape with his life, the bullet shattering the bone in his upper left leg. If he had gone through the front door of the abandoned building, the sniper would have had a perfect chest shot and would have killed him before he even got to his mate – who survived as well, fully recovered and forever grateful to Nate for saving his life.

Now, his instincts are telling him that something is going on with Molly Johnson. The lunch date with his wife and son will have to wait. Nate turns his horse and gallops off in the opposite direction.

Nate pulls on the reins, slowing his horse to a trot. The land here is drier and less grassy – more of a red clay earth, harsher, further away from the river system. Slowing to a walk, the horse carefully steps through some scrub as they near a small hut. It lies just off the thoroughfare, about half an hour from town. The hut sits right on the edge, where the plain country stops and the scrub begins. A little privacy for Elpida Sava's business: prostitution. Been in the area for some time now. Her father came here for the gold rush but was killed in a dispute over ownership of one of the biggest hauls. His wife and eldest daughter, Elpida, were left to fend for themselves and the two younger daughters. Elpida and her mother went into prostitution. They made a good living, supporting the two younger girls and giving them a good education away in Melbourne.

Cautiously, Nate looks around. He approaches from the back of the hut. The madam of the house may have a customer, and he doesn't want to barge in on anything. A robust woman, in her fifties at least, not at all pretty, stands in the doorway, her breasts on full display at the top of her corset. Her breasts are the best thing about her. Cigarette in hand, she exhales slowly, blowing a fine stream of smoke into the air.

Nate is startled. He wasn't expecting her to be standing there, let alone bare-breasted. He doesn't know where to look.

She smiles, pleasantly enough for a woman with no front teeth. 'New sergeant comin' to support local business? I'm flattered.' She hitches up her undergarment to cover her breasts.

Nate tips his hat, a little embarrassed. 'Here to ask you a few questions, madam.'

With a cheeky grin she asks, 'Before or after?'

Nate's not sure how to respond, so decides to get straight to it: 'When was the last time you saw Joe Johnson?'

Her smile quickly falls away. 'His wife, crazy bitch, came here wavin' her shotgun about! Must have been three months back now, or thereabouts. She walked in on us. Placed her Cowles & Dunn on his balls and threatened to blow them off if he didn't get up that very instant and get home! Rantin' and ravin' she was, about a bloody birthday ruined.' She mimics Molly screaming, '"Fuck her all ya want, but I asked ya for the boy's sake!" Something about her son's twelfth birthday.'

This has made things a little clearer. A domestic dispute. Could it have turned into something more? Something nasty? Or has Joe just up and left his crazed gun-wielding wife and the kids? Nate now knows he needs to get out to talk to Molly as soon as possible. But first he must stop Danny and his siblings from leaving town. He just might be able to get something more from the boy. He tips his hat, turns his horse and gallops away.

'Come back anytime! First one's on me!' Elpida throws her head back, laughing huskily. Her laughter turns into a heavy smoker's cough and she coughs up half a lung, spitting the bile onto the ground. Mountain life has sure hardened her.

In a cell in the Everton jailhouse, Danny lies on a single iron-framed stretcher-bed. Joe Junior, Henry James and Delphi play doctors and nurses, attending to their patient. They put their hands on Danny's chest. One puts an ear to his nose; another, a hand on his forehead. They look at each other, shaking their heads.

Then they hear Sergeant Clintoff calling from the front office area, 'Danny, can you come here please, son?'

Danny lifts himself up onto his elbows and peers through the bars to the other side of the room, where Father McGuinness, Miss Shirley and Nate stand huddled around his desk. Their conversation is hushed and he can't quite make out what they are saying. Now and then they throw a look back at the children.

Danny gets up slowly and heads out to them. Henry James is quick to take his place on the stretcher as Delphi starts the routine of hands to chest, ear to nose, hand to forehead, diagnosis not good.

Danny makes his way towards the desk. He's in no hurry: he knows he's in trouble – if not with these adults, he will be with his mother. He's said too much already. As he gets closer, his steps slow to a stop as he spots the poster of Yadaka on the wall. It doesn't have the friendly eyes he knows the real Yadaka to have. The eyes in the picture are fierce, enraged, murderous.

Miss Shirley breaks his focus. 'Come now – Sergeant Clintoff is a busy man.'

Nate hasn't missed a beat and looks where Danny is staring. 'How do you know him, Danny?'

Danny looks straight into the eyes of a curious Nate; the boy doesn't miss a beat either. 'I don't, sir.'

Nate has worked him out. When the boy lies he looks Nate straight in the eye; when he is telling the truth he looks away or down at the ground, or he can't hide his guilt and gives himself away. That was the pattern when they were talking around the horse earlier.

Nate gently pulls a chair out from the desk for Danny as he perches on the corner. 'Come, have a seat.' The boy sits, desperately trying not to be drawn to the poster. 'You've not long had a birthday. Twelve?'

The question catches Danny by surprise. Nate watches him closely, reading his reaction. Danny's mind travels back to his birthday night. He is peeping through a crack in the wall, his eyes filled with fear. He hears a voice in the distance, gentle and caring. 'Danny?'

It's Nate, bringing him out of his memory. Danny looks down, fiddling with his fingers. 'Yes, sir. About three months back.'

Nate lets that sit for a moment. The room is still and suddenly, to Danny, airless. Beads of perspiration form on his top lip.

'Can you tell me about your birthday night?' Danny can't hide his concern at how much Sergeant Clintoff seems to know. He locks eyes with the officer, taking a deep breath. Here comes the lie, Nate knows, but he'll play along with the boy.

'They sang happy birthday. Us kids played a bit. Ma sat knittin' ... Da drinkin' ... We went to bed and slept like logs, didn't hear a thing.'

And there it is: 'Didn't hear a thing.' Something did happen.

Nate straightens up, trying not to appear too eager. 'What things might you have heard on a night like this, Danny?'

The boy can't hide it anymore. He looks off to nowhere as the memories come flooding back.

I lie in bed, awake. Scared. I can hear thumpin' coming from outside, and I flinch with each thud. Everything's muffled – groans, moans, gasps, whimpers. And it's comin' from my Ma. There's a crack in the wall by the door, so I creep out of bed to see for myself . . .

My da towers over Ma, who is curled up on the ground trying to protect herself as he lays into her, punch after punch. She doesn't cry out, probably for fear of waking the little ones. I'm frozen, don't know what to do. Once before I came to Ma's rescue and Da slung me so hard I hit my head and was sick for days. Ma swore she'd never let that happen again, and I know that's why she's not makin' a sound, takin' the blows with as little fuss as possible, not wantin' to draw me in. But I wish it were me he was beatin'. Not her. Please not her.

Danny is rattled by the memory but does his darnedest to fight his emotions. He fiddles with his fingers, pretending to pick at some loose skin on a nail. 'The usual, sir.'

'And what's that?' Nate gently asks.

Danny takes a moment, getting his emotions under control. The boy slowly lifts his head to bring his eyes to meet Nate's. 'Wild dogs barkin' in the hills. Crickets. Distant owl. Alligator dreamin' – he whines in his sleep. And Da . . . well, when he's drunk, he . . .'

'Yes, Danny?' Nate says, leaning forward.

Danny's eyes haven't moved off Nate's. 'Farts a lot, sir.'

From the cell the other children giggle. Nate knows Danny is lying but he smiles, humouring the boy. 'I only want to help your ma, Danny.'

At this, Danny appraises Nate. Maybe he is a good man. Maybe Danny should tell him everything he knows about that night. But he promised himself he wouldn't. He never would. Not even to his own ma.

Nate turns back to the McGuinnesses, who are annoyed at what they see as the boy's arrogance. He glimpses the poster of the wanted Aboriginal man and tries another angle. 'He's wanted for a very brutal murder, Danny. Eight people, he killed – a mother and her children.'

Danny snaps a look at Nate. He won't believe it. That's not the man he knows Yadaka to be. From the boy's disappointed reaction, Nate realises Danny knows a whole lot more than he's saying. Nate needs to get out to Molly Johnson's. 'Over the range from your place. I'm worried about your mother. I'm thinking I'll take a ride out there myself.' He leaves a pause for Danny's benefit. 'Talk to your mother. Look around.'

Danny becomes a little anxious. *Look around?* There's great concern in his eyes now but he holds his tongue, totally confused about his feelings and what he knows to be the truth about Yadaka. But he is worried about his ma after learning this from Sergeant Clintoff. He can only hope she is all right, and trust his instincts regarding Yadaka's character. He looks back at the poster, and deep in his heart he knows Yadaka is not a bad man. He knows what bad men do, and Yadaka is nothing like his father. But . . .

Danny surprises them as well as himself with his reply: 'I think that would be a good idea, Sergeant Clintoff.'

The three adults turn to him. 'Why, Danny?' asks Nate.

Danny puts his head down and talks to the ground. 'She's alone and I worry for her when I'm away.'

Nate notes this as truth. He turns to Miss Shirley and says, 'Please take the children home and keep them safe. I'll return with their mother in the morning.'

Danny goes to say something else but Nate is already out the door. Danny has second thoughts – maybe he shouldn't have said that, not with the secrets, lies and ghosts that hover just above the surface of his ma's land like the first mist of winter. It's just too much for Danny. He heads straight back into the cell to his brothers and sister. Looking for solace and comfort disguised as the responsibility he feels to protect them, Danny gathers his siblings to him and in a hushed, gentle tone tells them of the plan: they will be heading back out to the McGuinnesses'.

Delphi looks quizzically at Danny and says, 'And tomorrow, we head home?' Danny can't answer. He himself is unsure. Worry and concern fill his eyes.

'Danny?' she asks again.

Nate races along the thoroughfare from town on horseback. Ahead of him is his property. He snaps the reins to drive his horse harder, fighting the urge to stop. As he draws nearer, he can't help himself and his eyes dart to the house.

Then he pulls hard on the reins, stopping the horse immediately. He takes in his new home, the chimneys: there's no smoke. *That's unusual.* The kitchen stove is always burning. He turns the horse and gallops towards the yard. The horse clears the front fence and they race around to the back. Before it even stops, Nate slides off. He hits the ground running midstride and sprints inside, favouring his blasted leg.

He rushes through the back door into the kitchen, breathing heavily, rubbing out the pain in his leg. The amount of horseriding he's been doing is certainly giving his injury a workout.

All is quiet. Too quiet. The fire in the kitchen stove is out. Nate's concern grows. He calls, containing his anxiety, 'Louisa?' No answer.

'Louisa! Samuel!' He runs to the bedroom. There on the bed are his wife and son, sound asleep. Relieved, Nate goes to them. Quietly and gently he perches himself on the edge of the bed, careful not to wake them. He looks at them lovingly and strokes his wife's face. She stirs. His hand is drenched with sweat and he realises she is sick with fever. She is extremely hot and sweating profusely. He grabs a wet washcloth from the bedside table and gently dabs at her forehead.

Louisa rolls over, about to throw up. 'Nate, bucket!'

He grabs the bucket just in time and Louisa heaves into it. He rubs her back. She lifts her head, wiping her mouth with the back of her hand, and says, 'Samuel . . .'

'He's right here,' Nate reassures her, but she quickly turns to the boy beside her and says, 'Nate, check him! Lift him!' Nate is more than a little alarmed by her concern. He lifts the boy and his son's body lies limp in his arms.

Louisa screams, 'Oh my God! Nate!' Her exertion almost causes her to faint. She turns and heaves again into the bucket, collapsing back onto her pillow.

Nate has swung around to the other side of the bed and puts his ear to the boy's chest, then a finger to his nose. Lifting the boy's shirt, he sees that his son is struggling to breathe, his diaphragm barely expanding with the shallow intake of breath. Nate takes a moment to think, knowing he won't be going anywhere near Molly Johnson now. His boy and wife need urgent medical attention. *I'll collect Molly tomorrow. The children will stay put at the McGuinnesses', as instructed.*

Molly won't be going anywhere – she's expecting her children home soon. Or he could get Trooper Leslie to go out and bring her in.

His greatest concern right now is his little family's health. Louisa and Samuel are in desperate need. Nate quickly wraps Samuel in a blanket and says, 'I'll get him to the doctor's and come back for you. Don't fret – rest. Samuel will be fine. You will both be fine. I'll see to it.'

With that he leans across and kisses his wife's forehead, 'I love you.' Then he hightails it out the back to his waiting horse.

'Hurry, Nate! Hurry!' Louisa only just manages to call out after him. She turns and heaves again into the bucket.

TWENTY-FOUR

The full moon finally peeks over the mountaintops, illuminating the landscape. On her verandah, Molly stares straight ahead, lost for words.

Yadaka stands before her dressed in her husband's pants, a shirt and the vest she mended the night before around the fire pit. His hair is damp and combed back. 'This all right?' he asks.

Molly still can't speak.

'Ya husband, seein' me in his clothes?'

'A pair of boots and ya could pass for a decent man,' she manages. Yadaka looks at his bare feet. She does have a point. Maybe Danny was right when he said a decent man has boots on his feet. In the attire Yadaka now wears, that statement kind of rings true.

Molly continues: 'Ya worked for me, and I paid ya in clothes. His clothes. Old clothes. That's what ya say. It's the truth.'

Yadaka nods and turns to leave.

'Wait.'

He turns back to face her. And, seeing Molly in the moonlight, he sighs with desire.

'I'll wax ya hair so it stays straight. The wet hair will dry. Your hair will curl. Sit.' She indicates the chopping block. Yadaka knows he should just go. *Leave, now!* But his heart tells him to stay. He removes the axe and puts it to the side and sits. He stares out at the big silver moon rising over the mountaintop. Like a spotlight, it beams into the front yard.

Molly has gone back inside to get the wax. She comes back with a small tin can in her hand, opens it and takes out a dollop, working the wax between her fingertips. She looks to where Yadaka is looking and hoarsely whispers, 'Full moon.'

'Good to walk by,' he replies. Both know that this symbol marks Yadaka leaving.

She walks slowly towards him, taking in his form and massaging the wax into her hands. Her voice almost inaudible, she says, 'Messes with a woman's mind.'

She steadies herself as she draws closer to him, steels herself as she reaches out and runs her fingers through his hair. Molly has never done this before, has never had these feelings bubbling inside her before either. Something has stirred deep within her. It must be the moon.

Yadaka's breath catches as her hand gently takes his hair, affected by her touch. The sensation is so simple but so effective. A gentle feminine touch – something he hasn't felt for a very long time.

Molly sighs deeply. It comes as an uncontrollable urge. She too is affected by their closeness. She shakes her head, dispelling the magic of the moon and the moment. A distraction she has to find, these urges she must hide. She takes in Yadaka's side profile as she works the wax into his hair. 'Ya features are quite fine.'

'White father.'

'Ya know him?'

'Don't think my mother even knew him.'

Molly nods to herself, absorbing this information. 'I didn't know my ma.'

She becomes a little annoyed at herself. She's never told this to anyone. Her husband knows, but only because her father warned him that she had no female influence growing up and might take some 'learnin'' to get her behaving in female ways. He meant sex, and Joe Johnson saw to that learning all right. The hard and violent way for Molly, unfortunately.

Yadaka interrupts her thoughts: 'You got any family?'

'Just my children. And before them just my da. Just Da and me. He would say, "We are all the family we need".'

This back and forth between them is coming all too easy now. She massages the wax into the back of Yadaka's hair. It isn't really working to straighten the curls, but she's trying. Molly secretly hopes he does make it home. She wishes no harm to him. 'She died giving birth to me. My ma.'

Yadaka's intrigue pricks in disbelief. From things he has seen and heard about her life since he's been here, it's all sounding very familiar, and now this last piece of information ... Slowly Molly's story's fractured pieces are taking form for him.

He looks at her. He knows her. He smiles. 'It is you.' More for himself now, he goes through the evidence as the facts begins to fall into place. 'Molly, pet name to Mary. She died giving birth. Ginny May's visits, of course.' He shakes his head in disbelief.

'Beg your pardon?' Molly looks at him, puzzled. With his hair done, she comes around to stand in front of him.

Yadaka wants to tell her what he knows. Was he destined to stumble across this woman's path, landing on her very doorstep? 'That woman who was helping you, Ginny May. She is my adopted mother.'

This doesn't mean anything to Molly. 'Small world—', she begins, but he interrupts.

'On the night you were born, she held you in her arms while your father cried over your dead mother's body.'

'Gins help white women in childbirth all the time.'

'Ginny May kept the story alive about *her sister's* great love for a man of wrong skin.'

This grabs her attention. Molly can't believe what she is hearing.

Yadaka continues, very excited to share all he knows, all that Ginny May told him. This was her plan all along. 'Black Mary, "whitest gin around" – that's what the district folk would call her. Ginny May said she had red hair and fair skin but her Ngarigo features were strong. Black Mary worked as a cook for some drovers, and your da was one of them.'

Molly looks at Yadaka, flabbergasted. He takes the moment to spell it out as clear as he can: 'Your mother. She's black.'

Molly slaps him across the face, hard. 'How dare ya speak to me like that? I show ya some respect and ya take all the liberties in the world. You're done here!'

Yadaka knows he must keep pushing forward with the story with which he has been entrusted, despite Molly's rage. If he doesn't, there may never be another opportunity. As upset and disrespected as he knows Molly may feel right now, he continues. He must. 'Ginny May knew that Black Mary's love for the Scotsman was real, and his for her. They kept to themselves because no one would accept them.'

'Shut ya mouth!'

'Their love was deep as the highest peak to the lowest valley, and as wild as the Snowy River.'

'Stop!' Molly walks to her shotgun, which rests on the verandah post.

'Ngarigo, they're your family. No shame in that.'

She turns, cocking the shotgun and aiming it straight at him. 'Take ya filthy-talking mouth and get the fuck off my land! Go!'

Yadaka looks at her, desperation all over his face. Pleading for her to hear him out. 'Molly, please, there is no malice in the giving of this story. It's the truth, your truth. I was given it by a great woman. Part of my lore – our lore – is to share the stories so we live long into tomorrow and beyond. A story untold is a life not lived, and your mother, Black Mary, Waraganj, lived. Lived large in her short time.

'I mean no disrespect to you or your mother when I tell this next tale but I also heard a version from an old white farmer. He hired me to lend a helpin' hand in return for a meal and a place to rest for a while. The farmer told me about the young fair-skinned black woman with red hair. From a distance you were well and truly right to think she was white, but up close her nigger features were strong. The tale he told went like this – see, the white men in the district gave your mother the name "Black Mary" so that it was clear to all she was indeed a black woman and if they ever caught her . . .' His tone softens. 'If they ever caught her they could have their way with her.'

The old farmer quoted the sayings from others to Yadaka:

'A filly yet to be broke.'

'She runs wild like the brumbies.'

'Fights like a man.'

'Cunning as a black, though.'

Yadaka, feeling Molly's disbelief and bewilderment, is remorseful at delivering such an account. Nevertheless, he continues. 'These were just some of the things said about her. The farmer said he vaguely remembered that there was some talk about her being caught by a Scot. His wife had spoken about Black Mary and the Scotsman but that was years ago, and his wife was long gone by the time I arrived on the property. "It wasn't right to take one as ya wife," the old farmer said. "To have relations with was one thing. The norm to some. But to marry, they'd have had to keep that quiet and out of sight."'

Yadaka stands in front of Molly. She is seething at him. He tries one last time to get through to her: 'Ginny May kept those stories alive, of her sister's great love for a man of wrong skin. She told and retold that story to her youngest son, Bulburai, but he showed no interest in it. He knew it was forbidden by King Jimmy. I did ask Ginny May why she told me this story of her sister over and over, and she simply said, "Someone needs to know".'

Yadaka stares at Molly. Has he got through to her?

Those few seconds seem like a lifetime to Molly as she desperately tries to make sense of the many questions racing through her head. Hearing this story for the first time – her story – she just can't fathom it, not right now, anyway. Not with all that's happened. What good can come from knowing this? Known for being touched by the tar brush. And what about her children? What will they have to deal with? She must put her children first.

She manages to say, finally, 'I need you to go. Now. GO! GET! Go!'

Defeated, Yadaka turns to leave. But at that very second, through the scrub comes Trooper Leslie on horseback. His horse froths at the mouth – it has been ridden hard. Spencer Leslie swings down with no grace or style, stumbling, a clumsy hand on his pistol. The horse takes off. He looks very tired and flustered. 'I heard yelling. Is everything all right here?'

Molly quickly composes herself and thinks, *What more can happen tonight? This blasted full moon!* Good Lord, now she must deal with this. Like a skilled actress, she changes her demeanour in the blink of an eye and says, 'Yes, thank you.'

This does not go unnoticed by Yadaka and he quickly turns his back, fastening the top button of the shirt to hide his scar and the red markings from the iron collar he was wearing at his first meeting with Molly. The very thing she freed him from. And she prays in this very moment that he has buried that thing deep. He turns back to the trooper, standing with his head bowed like an obedient servant. He can play the game too. Has done so for many years. That's how he has survived.

Spencer fumbles for his small notepad in his top pocket, saying, 'Is this—' He finds the information he needs. Maybe he is just hesitating for effect. Or the adrenaline of the moment has clouded his mind of the facts. 'Is this the property of a Mister Joe Johnson?'

Molly, not missing a beat, is warm and inviting. 'I'm Missus Joe Johnson.'

Spencer continues with his line of questioning: 'Where is Mister Johnson?'

'He's in town getting supplies. He'll be home in the mornin', if ya care to come back then,' she replies.

Yadaka keeps his head down and stays quiet, trying to figure out a way to get out of the situation. But just as he comes up with an idea and lifts his face towards Molly, the full moon climbs above the treetops and throws a beam of light across his face. 'Missus?'

Spencer swings to face the black man, and on seeing his face realises it is the wanted man on the poster. The man wanted for the murders of the Edwards family, their Chinese house-hands, a trooper and a native police. *Good God!*

On seeing the trooper's reaction, Yadaka knows he's been recognised. He tells himself to remain calm and hopes Molly plays along. 'I'll attend to my duties out back, missus?'

Spencer can't believe his good fortune. If he brings the black in, it will win him some much-needed credibility. 'Don't you move!' he orders. Hand shaking, he tries to hold his pistol steady, pointing it straight at the most wanted man in Everton: a runaway murderous heathen savage.

TWENTY-FIVE

Molly's three youngest children lie head to toe in a big bed in the spare room at the McGuinnesses'. Their heads rest on luxurious soft ruffled pillows, and fluffy blankets are pulled up high. As if on a cloud, they sleep sound. Behind them, at the window, stands Danny, worry etched on his little face. He looks at the full moon climbing slowly in the sky, then at his sleeping siblings. *What should I do?*

He's worried about his ma and about Sergeant Clintoff going out there. He was so foolish to say what he did. *Bastard boy!* he thinks to himself. But the night is still young. *If I leave now, I'll get home by midnight.* All Danny knows is that he must do something. He creeps over to the bedroom door and cracks it open to see Miss Shirley and Father McGuinness sitting with a distinguished older gentleman – a man of authority, perhaps?

It's Judge Eisenmangher, writing on a piece of paper. As usual, Miss Shirley holds court.

'Judge Eisenmangher, I've never shared those stories before because I could never get a sober confession from her father, but I do believe them to be true. His truth serum was rum. I've always known there's more than meets the eye to Molly Johnson.'

On hearing his mother's name Danny steps away, his back pressed to the wall in shock knowing that there is a judge in the house and that Miss Shirley, in a degrading tone, is talking about his ma. His ma has never done anything to warrant this from her. His brothers have been better behaved on this visit: Miss Shirley said so herself. He peers back through the crack in the door to the parlour. Miss Shirley continues.

'I heard what people said about the fair-skinned gin with the freckles and red hair. They called her Black Mary and talked about how Molly's father, Jock Stewart, chased after her. Disgraceful, really. I don't see or understand the appeal.'

Tut-tutting, Father McGuinness speaks up. 'Now, Mother, who are we to judge? Leave that to the good Lord and Judge Eisenmangher here this evening.'

Miss Shirley can't help herself – she loves an audience. 'Still, mixing like that. Bringing confusion to the children from that sort of relationship. Thank the Lord there was only one. She might have been one of the first in the district to be born of mixed blood but unfortunately she won't be the last.' Turning her nose up at the thought, she pauses as she adds up something in her head, then says, 'Black Mary was about six years younger than me. Yes, six. She was sixteen when she first was seen. I was twenty-two. And I remember well the Edwards family was her first encounter with whites. And let me tell you, there's a tall tale there to be told.'

Without taking a breath Miss Shirley launches straight in. 'Black Mary's father was Charles Edwards!'

'Mother!' Father McGuinness interjects, narrowing his eyes to make his point. 'There is no evidence to this hearsay. "If any man among you seem to be religious, and bridleth not his tongue, but deceiveth his own heart, this man's religion is vain." James 1, verse 26.'

Annoyed by the interjection, Miss Shirley sarcastically replies, 'Forgive me, Father, for I have sinned.' Not missing a beat, she continues, 'And if Sergeant Clintoff's assumption is right, that she's harbouring that black murdering savage out there … well, then. What is left for us to do?'

She pauses for dramatic effect, 'Octaroon is what I'd call her children. They need urgent help, Judge Eisenmangher,' pleads Miss Shirley.

Need help? Danny thinks. *From you, by the sound of it.*

The judge finishes his note, and with an elaborate swirl of his pen, he signs his name, folds the letter neatly in half and hands it to Miss Shirley. 'For their safety, the children's removal is authorised.'

Danny's eyes widen in fright.

Removal? What does that mean? Move to where, and why? We have to go home to our ma. She's waitin' for us. Tomorrow, we will be goin' home. Why would anyone do that? Take us from her? She's a good ma, does all she can for us. She loves us, tells us every night. And puts up with so much from …

Danny quickly and quietly shuts the door. He knows he has to do something. He looks at his sleeping siblings, and then at the window.

The pen wielded by Judge Eisenmangher rests on the McGuinnesses' dining table – the same table around which Molly Johnson's children were fed. In the name of their loving Lord Jesus and their Christian charity, the McGuinnesses have given Molly respite and time for herself, like any mother who struggles to make ends meet deserves. She's only human.

But the ink spat from the poison pen has the same power as the double-edged sword of reason and law: tonight the pen did not help but hurt, cutting deep, slicing, severing ties that will be long lost and forever gone. The simple swish of the pen is all it took to wreak havoc, destroy a family. Molly Johnson's family.

TWENTY-SIX

The full moon has climbed further in the night sky. Through the treetops it spills shafts of light over Molly's plateau, giving this heated moment far more attention than either Molly or Yadaka wants. With his hands on his head, scars and red welts on his collarbone, Yadaka kneels before the trooper.

Spencer Leslie reads him his rights: 'In the Queen's name I arrest you for the murder of Missus Edwards and her three children, for the murders of Trooper Phillips and native policeman Dempsey Buckskin.'

Molly is taken aback when she hears this. Yadaka never mentioned the deaths of the men. His eyes flick to her and he sees her disappointment. He wishes he had a moment to tell her his side of the story. They hold each other's gaze for a split second before it is interrupted by the trooper.

'And you, Missus Johnson, I'll need you to accompany me to the lock-up for questioning.'

Molly knows she can't go anywhere. She won't go anywhere. Her children will be home soon, and she needs to be here for them, always. 'I didn't know he killed—'

'Regarding the whereabouts of your husband,' interrupts Trooper Leslie, gloating in his own sense of superiority.

This silences Molly. Her facade drops for a moment as she contemplates what this means for her and her children.

'There has been some concern from your husband's work colleagues. He didn't make the drove. They found his horse running with brumbies. Put down the gun, Missus Johnson, please.'

Molly stands frozen in the moment. As he looks on, Yadaka suddenly makes sense of Molly's reactions to certain things over the past few days. The story about shooting the bullock, and how that affected her. The hat Yadaka found in the shed, stuffed behind things, and how she fell apart seeing him wearing it. He observes Molly's stress building.

'My children will be home soon!'

Yadaka knows he must do something to distract the trooper so Molly can steady herself. He wants to help her. Spencer's continuous rambling is sending Molly into a further state of anxiety. Yadaka knows she will not let anything come between herself and her children, and he must do something before she does. He decides to stand up, risking being shot on the spot, but it's a risk he is willing take for this woman. He reasons this may be the better option for him anyway. His future looks grim now that this trooper has arrived.

He only killed the other trooper and the native policeman because he was being arrested for something he did not do. He'd had enough of this treatment of himself and his people. He'd heard the stories: there would be no trial for him. It was live or die, and at that moment he chose to live. But in the end, was that decision worth it?

It was. He's met Molly Johnson and gifted her with her Dreaming, her origins – where she began. Yadaka realises that Spencer is not comfortable or skilled in confrontation. His trigger finger might slip. Yadaka knows he needs to be careful or he could get them both – him and Molly – killed by the panicked trooper.

Yadaka rises with determination, prepared for instant death. The trooper immediately brings his focus to Yadaka, as hoped. 'Stay down! I will shoot!' Fortunately for Yadaka he does not do so.

Perspiration runs down the trooper's face. He becomes more flustered as he attempts to keep the sweat from running into his eyes. *Don't these people know who I am, the authority I hold? First she does not obey my requests to put down her blasted gun, and now this black man defies me!*

Yadaka sees the trooper's angst and lowers his head in surrender.

'I can't go with ya. My children,' says Molly again.

The trooper brings his attention back to her. 'I'm under strict orders to bring you in.'

'No, my children!'

Yadaka tries again to bring the focus back to him: 'Just take me, boss.'

Trooper Leslie is almost at the point of losing his self-control. 'Quiet!' His pistol is swinging back and forth between them, trusting neither. Voice strained, he begs, 'Missus Johnson! Please!'

Molly has whipped herself into a frenzy. 'They need me!'

Gently, Yadaka takes a step towards the trooper, saying, 'Take me, boss.'

'Quiet! Stay down!'

'My children need me!'

'Take me, boss!'

'Please, Missus Johnson! The gun, down!'

'What will happen to my children?'

Yadaka's own anxiety is rising now. He can see where this is heading, and everything around him slows. Maybe it's a blessing for him as he calculates what to do.

The trooper turns sharply on his heels, stepping towards Molly, his pistol aimed straight at her head. Yadaka's instinct is to defend her, and he prepares to launch himself. Spencer yells, spit flying from his mouth, 'Shut! Up! Woman!'

Her eyes raging with fear and anger, Molly's body is tense and trembling.

Before me the trooper is no more. It's him! His hat! His fists! The glass shard! *The children! Think of the children!* I hear my soul scream. The fractured images that haunt me in my sleep have materialised. *Will this nightmare ever end?*

Yadaka has read Molly well. He doesn't want her to answer the question plaguing her right now with the action she intends. He sees the tension she has placed on her gun and knows what is coming. He finds his footing and launches himself at the trooper, hoping to knock him out of the way. *No more death!*

BANG! A shot rings out, echoing, bouncing back from the mountains in the silence of the night. Molly's world slows around her and to her horror the two men fall to the ground in front of her. She's unsure if it was she or the trooper who fired.

She snaps out of her moment of stupor, quickly checking that she has not been hit. Then she looks at her smoking gun, realising it was she who pulled the trigger of her trusty Cowles & Dunn. She stands horrified, her mouth gaping, knowing that one of the two men on the ground before her has taken the bullet. Time has stopped. Molly watches for movement among the entangled two.

Then Yadaka rolls away, springing to his feet. Catching his breath, he stands, still and in shock.

Molly can only stare at the dead trooper lying at her feet. And as quick as the sting of winter's arrival, she has turned cold, numb. 'Bury him deep,' she tells Yadaka.

TWENTY-SEVEN

The first full moon of winter has climbed higher in the night sky; it's an hour or so off midnight.

A small flickering flame dances in the fire pit before Molly. She stares vacantly at it, her shawl wrapped tightly around her. She holds herself in shock. Her broom and shotgun are beside her and the ground before her has been swept. There is no sign of the struggle with the trooper, the day's comings and goings erased. His blood has been covered up and all traces of him are gone, and the night's silence is broken only by the pleasant crackling of burning wood. The full moon shines down serenely on Molly. Somewhere overhead the powerful owl calls and Molly looks up and out into the darkness. The moon's beams now spotlight the branches of the snow gums, rendering the trees like spirits caught in time. She stares harder into them as if she has seen something.

Molly moves to reach for her shotgun but changes her mind as she investigates, her shawl falling away. She stops in her tracks, mesmerised by whatever has caught her eye. Her breath catches as she sees the young fair-skinned Aboriginal woman with the red hair – the woman who was with her under the water, the woman Molly reached for but it was Molly who was swept away before she could take hold. She almost glows in the moonlight, holding something in her arms. Molly's eyes find focus and she sees that the woman is holding two swaddled dead babies. Are these Molly's dead babies? Little Jack and Daisy? Who is this woman? Was Yadaka's story of the Aboriginal woman called Black Mary true? Is this her?

Molly does not move or speak. Neither afraid nor threatened, she's simply caught in this hauntingly beautiful moment. Her breasts start to leak milk. A warmth starts from deep within her, her motherly instincts ignited by the sight of this fair-skinned, red-haired Aboriginal woman and the swaddled babies. *Is this my mother? Mary?*

A cloud crosses the full moon, fracturing its shining beams, and the woman and the babies are gone. Breathlessly, Molly calls, acknowledging, 'Mary . . .' Only the sounds of nature fill the night, and again, the call of the powerful owl. The warmth Molly felt is replaced with emptiness. For a split second she felt whole, complete . . . not alone, her ma was here. She could have sat in that moment forever.

A gentle 'Missus?' comes from behind her. Out of the darkness Yadaka appears, leaning the shovel against the side of the shanty. He has buried the dead trooper deep, as ordered. Molly doesn't look at him. He continues slowly over to her, talking gently as he goes so as not to scare her. 'You all right missus?'

Molly stands in the middle of her front yard, wet patches on the fabric of her dress, her breastmilk flowing freely. She is too caught up in what she's just experienced to realise what is happening. The cloud clears the full moon and its beams shine on Molly, bringing her back. She becomes aware of her leaking breasts, which she quickly covers with her hands as she moves to grab her shawl and shotgun. Taking them, she runs inside, embarrassed, and closes the door behind her.

Yadaka watches after her. He isn't sure how to respond.

Women's business is not my place. But I can't leave her – somethin' is terribly wrong for her to shoot a man of the law. That's not the Molly Johnson I know and respect. That's a woman deeply hurting and distressed, a woman extremely traumatised. That's a big hurt she's feeling, and overwhelmingly painful to contemplate. But ... I also know it's for the best. For both of us. The thought of leaving her tears at my heart.

Come out, Molly, and stop me. Say you need me to stay – to protect you.

Yadaka waits, but there is nothing – not a sound – from inside. And then he chuckles to himself. *As if Molly Johnson would say that. That's Molly Johnson, a drover's wife – she's been fendin' for herself most of her life ... all her life. She's not going to stop now.*

Unseen by Yadaka, Molly peers through one of the cracks in the wall from inside, desperately holding herself back from undoing the latch to her front door. She wishes he would just leave before she does something foolish like running into his strong arms and holding on forever. If she allows herself to do this, what will it mean? To herself? Her children? Him? Their lives?

She pinches her forearms, hard, to snap these silly ideas from her head. She needs to think. She needs to get rid of him. It's too dangerous to have him here. Finally, she thinks of something that will make him leave. It will hurt him deeply and get him hanged if he is caught. But he'll survive. He'll get home. He'll make it. She believes that – she has to.

Yadaka makes as if to leave but stops himself and looks back at the house one last time, hoping, waiting for ... nothing. There is no movement from inside. Time for him to leave.

His steps are slow and laboured, but as he reaches the old woodheap the front door opens and Molly steps onto the verandah, her bravado back, her shawl wrapped tightly around herself, holding herself at bay. Yadaka turns back, hopeful.

There's an awkwardly long pause, each waiting for the other to speak. Finally, Molly breaks the silence: 'You'll be my savin' grace if I can blame you ... for all of this. The trooper. My Joe.'

Yadaka is taken aback by the audacity of her request. But then it hits him: Molly has brought her husband's name into proceedings.

'I'm sorry, but my children – they need me, they need their ma.' Yadaka stands dumbfounded. 'I'd never just kill for the sake of it, but fight for my children, fight for my life – I will. Make no excuses for it.'

'Is that what you did? With your Joe?' It's all beginning to make sense for Yadaka.

The question almost brings Molly undone. Her effort to keep the secret hidden from others – but more so from herself, so life can be normal for her children – and the enormity of holding it in makes her buckle under the weight of being asked this simple, caring question. It has a profound physical effect on her, and she grabs at the rail to steady herself. Her face softens, she breathes deeply, and then it all comes flooding out: 'I buried his boots beside him, under the woodheap. Ya can't bury a man without his boots.'

Yadaka hears her perfectly but does not make a fuss about what she is saying. He looks down at the old woodheap and it's obvious now that the dirt mound is a grave. He looks back at her, asking, 'Joe is there?' and pointing to the mound.

'The children were gonna be up soon ... It's shallow, that's why the mound's there. Just stacked the last of the wood on top. Alligator fought off the wild dogs that came diggin'. Smell wasn't too bad, dependin' on which way the wind was blowin'. But there's always somethin' dyin' around here.'

Sensing this is what she needs, Yadaka remains quiet and gives her his full attention.

'He's buried there with his boots beside him. Take them.' Yadaka is unsure of what to say. Molly continues: 'Less attention to ya if ya wearin' boots.'

'No, thank you.'

'Might give you a chance if you're stopped. Use ya white name.'

He doesn't mean to, but he looks at her disapprovingly – and Molly sees it. 'Whatever ya gotta say or do to stay alive. That's how I see it.'

Silence falls, but the easiness between them remains. They move a little closer to each other. He can see that a weight has been lifted from her: the burden of the death of her husband has been released. No judgement made, just the understanding of two people who have suffered at the hands of others.

Yadaka isn't interested in details of how she did it – he kind of guesses, understanding why. He's relieved he's helped her to rid herself of the guilt. She looks out into the night. With her guard coming down, maybe he could ask now. Would she think him foolish?

He swallows hard, emotion caught in his throat, and whispers, 'Come with me.'

Yadaka's question snaps Molly back to reality fast. Her peace is short-lived as she realises what he is asking. 'Become a black?' she asks in disbelief.

'You are. And you know it.' Molly isn't sure how to respond, but Yadaka doesn't give her time to answer. 'That's why Ginny May was there for you. She is your family. Your children's family.'

'It's hard enough being a woman, let alone a black woman,' Molly says, frustrated by him and his ludicrous question. *Or is it?* She heads inside but leaves the door open, which encourages Yadaka to keep talking.

He gives her directions to where he will be holing up for the winter: a cave. North-east, two-and-a-half days walk from here. If she chooses to follow him, she'll come to the Great Waterhole, where she needs to keep to the right. He tells her she'll hit a bald patch, 'like someone cleared a perfect circle. Keep to the left of that. A little further on there's three big boulders, they look like emu eggs. It's there. Just beyond them. The cave. Food, blankets, shelter, and in the spring . . . people. Your people.'

There's silence as he hopes for a positive response. 'That's where I'm headin'. I'll be there.'

Silence again. Nothing comes from Molly inside the shanty.

It's time for him to go. He can't push his luck any further. He starts off again, but Molly calls from inside: 'The boots. Please take them, for ya safety.'

She comes to the verandah, clears her throat and whispers, 'You're a good man. Please.' She looks beautiful, and so vulnerable that Yadaka can't help but oblige her. He heads back towards the mound. Molly points to where the boots are buried, and he starts to dig. He doesn't have to dig too deep before he feels the boots and pulls them out. He holds up the left one and sees that the heel is worn down, just as Danny described. He takes them over to the log by the fire pit, dusts them down and pulls them on.

Molly can't watch – it's all become too much for her. She is almost sick with emotion. She heads back inside but leaves the front door open again. Yadaka watches her go and reads the open door as an invitation, perhaps? Is he getting to her? Can he try another way to win her over? He just wants her to say she'll catch him up with her children. *Yes, that's it – the children.* He knows how to win her over.

'Can I call on Danny, say, in six months' time?' he asks.

Molly stays inside but calls, 'Please, it's too dangerous.'

'I can take Danny on his first kill with his spear.'

Molly comes out onto the verandah with a small food package wrapped in cloth and tied with string. The sight of Yadaka in the moonlight takes her breath away – with the boots on, he cuts a fine figure. She takes a moment to steady herself, then steps from the verandah and goes to him. 'There's been enough killin' around here to last us all for a very long time.'

She hands him the package and quickly steps away, putting distance between the two of them, not trusting herself. She heads out into the yard, looking up at the full moon. *It sure is playing havoc with my mind and emotions tonight.*

'Thinkin' men's business. I promised Danny,' says Yadaka. 'And I can take you and your daughter on a walk. Where the Snowy starts to widen, there's these beautiful wildflowers ... Should be bloomin' by then.'

Molly turns to face him. He stands right behind her. Their eyes lock, sensual tension thick between them. A man and a woman, no divide, standing in the truth of the moment.

There's a glint in Molly's eyes. Has she had a change of heart? Is he reading her right?

Molly can't believe they have got to this point. *What the hell is happenin'?* She wants to speak her mind about what can't happen and what shouldn't happen, but all that escapes her lips, in a breathless whisper is '... Yadaka.'

She said my name. He's won her over. He can't help but smile on hearing his name on her lips. *Her lips, perfect.* He inches forward. Nothing else matters. Nothing can take this moment from them. His hand reaches for her, unsure, hesitant, then falls away.

Dammit, I can't move. Do I really want to walk away?

Their breathing becomes shallow. Yadaka steps forward again and his face drops to hers. *Her lips.* Brave of him to make a move – but he will wait for her now. All the awkwardness of a first-time lovers' encounter. Molly finally shifts her head ever so slightly towards him. *There it is*, Yadaka thinks. Should he kiss her now?

A gruff voice speaks from the dark of the shanty: 'There's been enough killin' around here, eh? So I've heard. And I'm bettin' you two might know a little more.'

Yadaka spins to face whoever this is. Molly steps aside to see a rugged stockman, built like a bullock, with a full red beard, standing in the doorway of her shanty, full of bravado, his rifle in hand. Yadaka moves to step forward. 'Don't move, ya black bastard. I'll put a bullet through ya fuckin' head.'

Molly boldly steps forward and says, 'State ya business!'

The stockman moves from the verandah and crosses the yard to them, shotgun in hand. 'I drive with Joe, except this drove he didn't show. First time in eight years. And I felt obliged to drop by and see if my old mate's all right.'

Yadaka's eyes haven't moved from the stockman. His stance is wide and sturdy and he's ready to pounce and defend if need be. But he must be careful.

The stockman continues, right in Molly's face: 'And on hearin' what I just heard, I'm more than a little worried.'

Molly holds her facade, strong and defiant. 'No need to be, Mister ...?'

'Parsen. Robert Parsen.'

'No need for your concern, Mister Robert Parsen.'

Parsen takes in Yadaka's appearance. 'Who the fuck did ya kill to get them clothes?' He steps up to Yadaka and the two men lock eyes, inches from each other's faces. 'You dare look a white man in the eye, Jacky?'

Yadaka diverts his gaze to the ground immediately, not wanting to start any trouble. But he's well aware and prepared for it. He knows how to play the game. He has to, for both their lives.

'I find your facial expressions inappropriate for a nigger.' With that, Parsen knees Yadaka in the balls, hard. Yadaka falls to the ground and Parsen sees that the Aboriginal man has Joe's boots on. He recognises the worn-down heel.

'Ya wearing Joe's boots, ya bastard!' Parsen takes aim at him.

Molly propels herself over Yadaka. 'No! Wait! I gave them to him for the work he did!'

'Get off him! Ya got no shame, ya harlot!'

Molly gets up, full of fight. 'I beg ya pardon?'

Yadaka, still recovering from the kick to his balls, lies on the ground in great pain, hoping that Molly's reaction won't provoke the stockman to end both their lives.

'You heard me. Now where's my mate? Where's Joe?' Parsen asks Molly.

'Gone. Left me. All alone with the children. No food, no nothin'. And my wee one dead, dead from all the worry. This man offered to help, and I needed help. And for his time I gave him Joe's boots.'

'Well, what the fuck's Joe got on his feet?'

'Not my concern! I found him in a compromisin' position with the whore due west. Ridin' 'im she was, and it wasn't fuckin' side-saddle.'

Parsen bursts out laughing. Molly's not sure where this is going. Yadaka has partly sat up now, still in pain.

Parsen continues laughing as he walks towards Molly. He gets up in her face again, becoming deadly serious, dead fast. 'I don't believe a fuckin' word you say. See, I found your Joe's horse runnin' with brumbies. As ya should know, losin' ya horse is a sure sign somethin' ain't right.'

Molly is riveted to the spot. Is it out of fear or bravado?

Parsen continues: 'A man from these parts goes nowhere without his horse, hat and boots. Unless he's dead, of course.'

Joe Johnson lies dead and rotting no more than a few feet away. Molly and Yadaka both know it, but give nothing away.

Parsen's gaze shifts from Molly to Yadaka. Has he called their bluff? He can't believe the audacity of the woman, standing before him eye to eye. *Doesn't this bitch know her place?* Despising her for it, he raises his rifle and stabs her hard in the ribs. Something cracks and Molly gasps with the pain, and stumbles back. Parsen follows through with a backhander, sending her stumbling further across the yard.

Yadaka struggles to get up. Parsen takes aim at him and pulls the trigger, but the shotgun jams. This gives Yadaka a chance. It is now or never and he throws himself at Parsen. The two men wrestle, twisting and turning across the yard towards the fire pit. Parsen has the upper hand as Yadaka is still recovering from the kick to his groin. Parsen headbutts Yadaka, dazing him and forcing him further back, stumbling over the log. He falls flat on his back and Parsen brings the butt of his rifle down hard, slamming it into Yadaka's face repeatedly. Yadaka's legs twitch with the repeated hits to his face, then he is still, his legs dangling lifeless over the log.

Parsen catches his breath, sucking hard to take in oxygen. Molly has managed to get up slowly, and just as Parsen pauses to check his rifle or perhaps reload to shoot Yadaka dead, she throws herself at him and wrestles for it. Not wanting to take his hands off his gun, he headbutts her, sending her to the ground.

Dazed, Molly lies foxing, giving herself time to work out her next move, to help herself and Yadaka. She has to think quick and sensibly – they could still both end up dead. What can she say or do to turn this around? *Think, woman. Think!*

There is movement behind her and she turns slightly. To her horror, she sees another, younger stockman. It's John McPharlen. He steps into the cleared area of the front yard. *Is he wearing a woman's skirt? What kind of fool is he? What is this in aid of?*

John McPharlen holds one of Yadaka's killing spears. 'Look at this!' he yells. He jumps up on the chopping block and starts to dance around, mimicking an Aborigine. He chants but his words mean nothing, just a lot of gibberish. It is a crude, degrading display. McPharlen laughs at himself, showing his rotten teeth. He finally stops his tomfoolery and looks around. He realises that something has happened here. 'Where's Joe?' he asks, then calls, 'Joe, we brought ya horse back!'

Parsen shakes his head, still finding his breath. He manages to get out, pointing towards the log, 'Rope this black bastard up.'

McPharlen peers over the log and gives a yelp of joy at the prospect of having a black man at his mercy. He drops the spear and, pulling a rope from his belt, takes Yadaka's legs and binds them. 'How many will he make?'

'Thirty-eight.'

'Is that all?'

'I'm not gettin' paid.'

Molly has been watching. She works to calculate her next move, red welts marking her face; snot and blood streaming from her nose.

McPharlen stops what he is doing and takes a closer look at the left boot with the worn heel. 'Hey, Joe's boots.'

Parsen waves the comment away as he heads to the water barrel and draws himself a drink. 'What took ya so long?'

'Had to take a shit.'

Molly looks at the spear, but it lies too close to McPharlen. Then she sees the axe at the base of the chopping block. Yadaka removed it when he sat for Molly to do his hair. If only she had simply said yes to going with him. Would they have been in a less vulnerable state? They may have seen or heard the stockmen coming, giving them time to prepare for this attack. But what good is 'should have, could have' now?

She slowly rises, as quietly and as stealthily as she can, even though her broken ribs pain her greatly. She steadies herself, then lunges with all her might at the axe. Sweeping it up, she lets out an almighty guttural 'Arrrrhhhhh!'

Molly doesn't see it, but from behind the snow gum, there is movement. Someone is there! Is it help? Is it Sergeant Nate Clintoff? Is he planning his move to intervene?

It's Danny, sweat running from his brow. He tries to catch his breath as quietly as he can. He has just arrived from the McGuinnesses'. Hearing the ruckus, he ditched his horse and silently made his way up to the old snow gum and hid behind the womanly curves of its trunk. He watches his ma and the men, deeply confused as to what has happened. But more so why it is happening. The men look vaguely familiar, although it's hard to tell as they have their hats pulled low, casting shadows across their faces. He has ridden out a couple of times to see his da off, and thinks they might be the men his da works with. But with only the moonlight to light their faces, he is unsure.

Danny watches them run either side of his ma and position themselves behind her, laughing at her attempt. He watches as she struggles to keep the axe aloft, her breathing shallow and rapid. He feels her pain. He hears Parsen say, 'Put it down, or I'll put a bullet through ya.'

Danny sinks to the base of the gum, frozen with fear. He wraps his arms around his legs and pulls them tight to his chest, praying for his ma to do as the man asks. He hears the same man say, 'You're a fuckin' disgrace! Riskin' everything for a black!' Danny takes a quick look and sees where Parsen is pointing. Behind the log he sees the legs of the gentle, caring and honourable man he knows as his friend. He is fearful that Yadaka may already be dead. Blacks can be shot on sight out here.

Danny has become very emotional and is totally at a loss as to what to do. Then he hears what the other man, McPharlen, says next, and a cold chill runs through him, as if death itself has sat down beside him: 'Ya gonna shoot 'er?'

Danny's eyes fill with tears. Parsen mumbles something but Danny can't make it out. The silence gets the better of him and he takes another look. With his mother releasing a gut-wrenching, 'Aaaaaaahhhhh!', Danny sees her bury the axe deep into the chopping block, surrendering.

The fear in Danny has paralysed him. He bites down hard on his bottom lip – so hard that he draws blood. He closes his eyes tight and tears stream down his cheeks. He turns away, unable to bear witness to what might happen next. He hears scuffling as the men move about but doesn't want to open his eyes – he's too afraid. He's walked into his worst nightmare. He thought what he witnessed with his own da and what his da did to his ma in his drunken rage was bad, but this here tonight . . .

He hears his ma begging, 'My children, please! My children!'

With tear-filled eyes, snot running from his nose and blood seeping from his lip, Danny peeks around the tree trunk again. He wants to run to his mother and protect her, like he tried to all the other times with his father, but he knows he is no match for these men. *But one day I will be.* The man with the red beard grabs his ma and delivers punch after punch to her face.

After the first punch, Molly is numb to the pain. She only feels the impact to her body, the jolt of the force, fist to bone. There's a slight twinge of pain if he punches in the same spot or over her open wounds. He finally lets her go and she falls to the ground like Delphi's rag doll. Falling on her broken ribs, she can't take anymore and fleetingly – and for the first time in her life – she wishes death would take her. The other man strides towards her, baring his rotten teeth. He spits on his hand, burying it down the front of his pants, and plays with his cock, arousing himself. He kicks at her legs, making space, then lowers himself on her, ripping at her undergarments.

Danny, traumatised, can't watch anymore. He turns away, placing his hand over his mouth to stop any noise escaping. McPharlen plunges himself deep into Molly, raping her.

Danny runs! Like a startled hare, he bounds off into the night.

And the powerful owl's haunting call echoes around the mountain range.

The full moon sits directly above. It is just on midnight. An eeriness hangs in the air. Danny stands stock still in the middle of the front yard, staring straight ahead at Yadaka hanging from the snow gum, silhouetted by the full moon, his da's boots only an inch from the ground. Yadaka's face is the ash grey of death. The white branches are outstretched like spirits stilled in their escape. It's beautiful and devastating.

Behind Danny there is a noise. It's Molly, stirring. She realises there is someone beside her and, jumping with fright, scurries away. The boy stays mesmerised by death hanging before him.

Molly finds her focus and realises it's her son. She follows his gaze, her swollen, tear-streaked face stained with dried blood, snot and dirt. Numb of any emotion, she stares at Yadaka's lifeless body, hanging still and stiff.

After a moment Danny speaks. 'He dead, Ma?'

Molly says nothing but blinks a few times, trying to find her thoughts.

Danny can't take his eyes off his dead friend. Silence. Nature mourns this moment, deathly silent. Then, ever so softly, the sound of the creaking rope. The rope is very short; Yadaka's neck is jammed up against the branches of the stout tree . . .

The sturdy tree's limbs outstretched, waiting to take the weight of winter . . . the weight of you . . .

'Two of ya da's mates . . . stopped by this evenin' . . . They brought word about ya da . . .'

'They did this.' Not a question, but a knowing.

'On the drove, up in the high country, ya da's horse slipped—'

'Stop, Ma.'

'Hittin' his head . . . dead. Somethin' like that.' Molly hates herself for her lies and fights to hold back tears.

'No, Ma!'

'It has to be.'

'Stop. I know, Ma.'

'Know what, son?'

'Not ya fault, though.'

Molly stares at him, confused, as Danny continues: 'Not a very happy night for my birthday . . .'

The boy is numb to the horror, numb to all of it. Emotionally drained. He takes his mind back to his birthday night, the night before his da was to leave for the drove.

His ma had promised a family dinner to celebrate the birthday of her eldest son. Turning twelve was important, she believed, and she wanted to do something nice for him.

All the children were in bed. The younger ones were sound asleep, but Danny could never sleep on nights like tonight because he knew all too well that after his da got his belly full of whiskey he would start on his ma. And tonight there was plenty for his da to be angry about. Times before, his da didn't need a reason to start on his ma. But tonight, his da felt like he had all the reason in the world to lash out at her for her behaviour earlier in the day.

His da's repeated mumbling and yelling coming from outside had Danny sitting on the edge of his bed the whole time. He wished his father would just go to sleep.

'Shamin' me manhood in front of a whore!' his da yelled clearly from time to time.

Joe couldn't and wouldn't let it go. Molly was just sitting there. She had tried a few times to go to bed but he held her there, laying his leg across her lap so she didn't dare move for fear he would ram it into her pregnant belly. She was six months pregnant, carrying small. She had told him, because normally he'd leave her alone.

Earlier in the night he'd sat down beside her, a sure sign he was looking for a fight. She'd attempted to get up and address a need of one of the children but he grabbed her by the arm, ripping her back. His other form of torment had been a headbutt to the temple. Dazed, she would sit straight back down. The headbutt she hated, because she never saw it coming and could never brace for the impact.

But tonight, something wasn't right. Danny could feel it. He was up and out of bed, peering through a crack in the wall.

Joe was a brute of a man, tall and robust. He had his hat pulled low, casting a shadow over his face. He was very drunk and his actions were slow and unstable. He stood over the chopping block with a bottle of whiskey in his hand. Swallowing the last of its contents, he wiped his mouth with the back of his hand and smashed the bottle hard against the block. The last remnants of whiskey ran down the side of the block, staining it like blood.

Danny comes out of his thoughts and sits on the ground beside his ma. He shakes the image from his mind and turns to Molly, but she is too guilt-ridden to look at him. Gently, Danny says, 'He was comin' for ya, Ma. Da was comin' to kill ya ...'

The memories are too strong, and his mind goes racing back.

The drover, with a jagged glass shard from the bottle in his hand, staggered towards a petrified Molly. Danny moved to find another crack in the wall so he could see his mother clearer. She clung to her shotgun, her body trembling all over, her face bruised and bleeding, dress ripped and torn. She just managed to get the words out: 'Joe, please. The children. Think of the children.'

Then he lunged at her, the glass shard aimed at her throat. Danny's eyes widened in fear and he whispered, pleading to his mother, 'Shoot 'im!'

A shot rang out.

Danny opens his eyes and sees his mother staring at him, deeply upset that he had to experience that, pained that he remembers it so vividly.

'One single shot, straight between the eyes, like the bullock ...' Danny's voice cracks as he comes to terms with what he's witnessed. 'Dead.'

Molly is at a loss. She tries with all her might to hold back her emotions. 'I'm so sorry, Danny.' She holds her arms open and he comes to her, sinking into her embrace, shielded and comforted by his mother's love. They hang on to each for dear life.

They sit there for a long time, holding each other. There is no crying, just relief.

Finally, Molly breaks the silence. 'Our secret, Danny.'

It's not a question but a statement, Molly doing what she needs to do to survive. Danny, forever the good abiding son, nods.

'Promise me.'

'Yes, Ma.'

She kisses him gently on the forehead and suddenly realises the other children aren't with him. Pushing him back to arm's length, she asks where they are. The boy is too scared to respond. Molly tries to read his silence. 'Did you say something, Danny? Where are ya brothers and sister?'

'Miss Shirley told that judge fella ... called us octaroons. What's that, Ma?'

Molly's world slows around her and her stomach turns. She remembers this word, or a word very like it. When she was eight years old and spending time with Miss Shirley, she heard Miss Shirley talking to another woman and it was this woman who was informing Miss Shirley about a place to send Molly away to. 'A home for this mixed-blood child, if you believe the father's drunken ramblings to be true, would be better for her. She can't be left to her father's devices. She needs cleansing of the filth that courses through her veins. The less she knows, the better. You only have to tell them she's a quadroon and she'll be sent away.'

Molly knows the word *octaroon* will get her children taken. It all makes sense now, with the story Yadaka told her. The pieces of her life's puzzle are falling into place. The past is making sense of the present.

Slowly a change comes over her. Her whole demeanour becomes that of a woman – no, a mother – scorned.

LEAH PURCELL

Silhouetted by the full moon, two people on horseback race across the plain. It's Molly and Danny, she with her trusty shotgun slung across her back. Joe's boots are tied to her duffel bag and she rides the trooper's horse. Danny has another duffel bag of supplies and is holding the killing spear Yadaka gave him. He's riding his father's horse.

Molly is focused. She drives her horse hard, digging her heels into its flanks.

Twenty-eight

Nate Clintoff stands frustrated at his bedroom window, looking out at the full moon. It's early morning but still dark. Soon dawn will be upon them. Louisa coughs violently and, waking herself, reaches across the bed and feels for her husband. He's not there.

'Nate?' Sleepily, she looks around the room.

Nate is lost in thought. All that he has learnt and heard plays over and over in his mind. Trooper Spencer Leslie has not returned with Molly Johnson. They should have returned a few hours ago if all went to plan.

'Nate?'

He finally speaks. 'You believed her?'

Taken aback by the absurd question, Louisa is bothered by his lack of concern for her. 'I'm fine. Thanks for your concern.'

Sighing with regret, Nate comes back to sit on the bed, taking his wife in his arms. 'I'm sorry. Can I get you anything?'

'No. Thank you.' Louisa shifts a little, seeking better eye contact. 'Who were you referring to?'

Kissing her forehead, Nate diverts his eyes. 'It doesn't matter.'

Louisa pushes herself away a little to get a better look at him and says, her voice slightly raised, 'Well, it must. You're standing at the window at this ridiculous hour of the morning.' She remembers her sick son, now sleeping peacefully beside them in his cot, and throws him a quick glance. She doesn't want to wake him – it's been a rough night. The boy gives a little sniffle. She coughs again, quickly burying it in her handkerchief.

Nate looks at her forlornly. 'Molly Johnson. She said, "Love watchin' my Joe canterin' . . . comin' home . . . wavin' his hat with joy . . ."'

Louisa takes a second, deeply concerned for Molly, and adds, 'No, I didn't. Somehow it didn't ring true – it was more like a vision she'd dreamt up to impress us. The look on her children's faces kind of gave it away, too.'

Nate shakes his head. He doesn't want to say it. 'I think she killed him. Murdered her husband.'

'Nate, what would make you say such a thing?'

'There was a smell around the woodheap. The bittersweet smell of death. I've smelt that before, in war – shallow graves, rotting flesh, death . . .'

There's silence between them, each conscious of the other's individual fight for justice.

Louisa considers, and says, 'A mother's love, Nate. Unconditional. Eternal. To protect. Stops at nothing for her children's sake. Not that I wish death upon anyone. But I'm sorry, Nate . . . there's only so much one can bear, before . . . Especially out here, and having no one to turn to for help.'

Tension rises between Louisa's cause and Nate's duty to uphold the law. Nate turns his gaze back to the window and the full moon, slowly falling to its slumber behind the western ranges.

Louisa, determined to make her point, continues. 'For the boy, Danny, to think it's a father's right to maim his own—' She stops herself, exhaling at the disgust she feels. 'I wouldn't blame her,' she adds, with great conviction.

Nate looks at her, bewildered. 'Really?' He's exasperated.

'Well, dammit ...' she exhales. 'I'm sorry, I still hurt ... and I'm still angry over my sister's death.' Emotion catches in her throat; she is frustrated now. 'I don't know ... Who knows, unless you are there in the moment. Dealing with it.'

Nate looks out the window again. 'Get some sleep,' Louisa whispers.

'I've tried.'

'It's that blasted moon.' Louisa fluffs up her pillow and lies down.

Nate is getting back into bed when he hears a distant rumbling. He listens closely and slowly turns back to the window. Louisa also picks up on the sound, lifting her head from the pillow to hear. Nate scampers over to the window.

Their house sits back from the main thoroughfare to Everton. The rumbling sound gets louder. Racing past on their horses are Molly and Danny, dust rising from the track. They are bound for Everton.

Molly's judgement is blinded by her urge to get to her children. She should never have come this way, but it's the only route in and out of Everton apart from through the thick scrub, and that would have delayed them. Molly wanted to slip in and out of town under the cover of night, but ironically, she has brought herself straight past the man who has been trying to see her for days. This time, her safety is not the only thing worrying him.

TWENTY-NINE

Out front of the McGuinnesses' stone cottage and the adjoining church, all appears well. The dull glow of a lamp shines through the closed curtain – left burning as a night light, perhaps?

'You have been good to me and my children over the years ...' Her demeanour deadly serious, Molly is clutching a piece of paper in her mouth as she speaks and ties and knots rope. 'And for that I am very grateful, but ...'

She is tying the hands of Miss Shirley and Father McGuinness. In shock, they sit gagged and bound before the fireplace in their nightclothes. There has been some resistance: furniture lies strewn over the floor and a glass vase has been smashed.

Molly moves closer to Miss Shirley, putting the paper in her face. 'Damn ya to hell for thinkin' ya know what is best for my children!' With that, she turns and grabs some blankets and a bag of food from the dining table. Miss Shirley begins to cry from fear and relief: their lives are being spared. Father McGuinness looks as if he might be having a heart attack. His eyes are wide and he is gasping for breath.

Molly throws the piece of paper in the fire and the flames eat at the condemning words – *octaroons ... removal necessary ... permission granted ...* – and the signature of Judge Eisenmangher. She leaves, slamming the door behind her.

Her children sit in the back of a wagon in the backyard. Molly distributes the blankets between them and puts the food in, pushing it all the way to the seat up the front. She takes a moment and sees the fear etched in their innocent little eyes. The sight of their mother's bruised and battered face, and the reality of what has just happened, has made them very scared. They were woken from their sound slumber by the sounds of raised voices and furniture being knocked over. Then Danny raced into the room urging them to get dressed and to grab blankets and pillows. The realisation hits her and Molly waves them over.

Her three youngest crawl over, still half-asleep but happy to see their ma and brother nonetheless. Molly hugs and kisses them and traces her hand gently over each face. Is she searching for their Ngarigo features? They don't understand her action.

Danny watches from the front of the buggy, moved by his mother's gentleness and deep love for her children. Although unclear about what is going on, the three are full of love and admiration for her.

Not wanting them to see her emotion, Molly takes a deep breath and looks at the sky. They all follow her gaze, wondering what she's looking at.

'Feel that stillness? That sharp cold? That sting in the air?'

Each child takes a moment to feel what their mother describes.

'Snow's comin',' she says. She closes her eyes, refreshed by the cold sting in the very early morning. She takes another moment. Another deep breath. The sharpness in the air hurts her lungs, the pain no doubt made worse by her cracked ribs. Shaking it off, she says, 'We gotta get goin'. And tomorrow, we can build a snowman and make snow cakes.'

She kisses Delphi's smiling face and tucks the little girl's rag doll in under the blanket, wrapping it tightly around her daughter. She instructs the two boys to get back under the blankets to keep warm, to keep quiet and to keep down. She checks the rope tied from the trooper's horse to the back of the wagon and throws a blanket to Danny.

'Wrap ya'self in this, son, over ya head. Anyone stops us, ya sick with influenza. Very contagious. Cough a few times when I say that. We're goin' for help. Not a peep out of the rest of ya's.' She throws a horse blanket over them, to conceal them. It now looks like she only has provisions under there, not children.

She climbs up and takes the reins, snapping them taut over the rump of the horse. The buggy moves off with a lurch. 'Now Danny, tell me again where we're headin'.'

The horses and sulky move down the dark back street as Danny goes through the detail of how to get to the cave, just as Yadaka told Molly in the hope she and her family would join him. Thanks to Yadaka, they will have a chance. Not just a chance of survival and a chance to remain as a family, but a chance to learn about who they are and feel the love and warmth of their large extended family. Even though the conditions will more than likely be pretty dire, at least the love from this new family will be pure. And hopefully they can have a few moments with this mob that are untouched and untarnished by the reality of the world they share.

Danny repeats the directions for his ma: 'Head north-east. When we get to the Great Waterhole, keep to the right. We'll come to a bald patch, keep to the left. Get to three boulders that look like three giant emu eggs – it's there.'

They have to go back through Everton to head out of town. The wagon moves slowly down the main street, Molly trying to keep the noise to a minimum.

'The cave is there with supplies and, in the spring, people.'

Molly nods her approval, seeming a little distant now. 'Ya tell them Black Mary. That's what ya say. They'll know who ya are then.'

'Who?' Danny inquires.

Molly takes a moment as she shapes the foreign words in her mouth, and then with pride says, 'They're our people, Danny. Family.' She looks down at him and finally smiles. Hope is clear in her eyes.

With that moment of relief, Molly's adrenaline is subsiding and the pain of her injuries is very obvious now. She hunches over, holding her cracked ribs, her breathing shallow.

'Ma?' says Danny, concerned for her. Spent, she turns to him. 'Ma, I won't never go a-drovin'.'

This breaks her heart. She reaches for him, pulling him into her as she kisses his forehead, and he softly exhales, saying, 'Always with you.' Molly is grateful she has such a caring and thoughtful young man as her son.

She must focus now as they approach the last establishment, the Stanlow Inn, before they are safely out of town. She looks to the road ahead and who should she see but John McPharlen!

Molly takes a second look and yes, it's him all right. She can't believe it. Her eyes glaze over with hurt and the world around her slows.

Danny sees his mother's reaction. He looks at McPharlen and knows exactly who he is. His fist tightens around the spear that lies beside him. This is the man he saw do that terrible thing to his ma. This is one of the men who hanged Yadaka.

McPharlen staggers into the shadows to take a piss. Molly slows the horse and hands the reins to Danny, saying, 'Go to the edge of town, leave that trooper's horse, and head straight for the cave. I'll catch ya's up. Ya hear me, Daniel Johnson?'

Danny goes to say something, but his ma shuts him down. 'Not a word now, Danny, please.'

He grabs his mother's arm to stop her jumping from the wagon.

'When I'm old enough, Ma, I'll come back to make the bastard pay. I promise. For you. For Yadaka. I'll put this spear right through him.'

Molly looks lovingly at her son – a look of deep, unwavering love. A knowing and an understanding passes between them. She feels for him, the predicament she has put him in, but scurries off into the shadows.

An emotional Danny reluctantly snaps the reins, and the wagon moves off down the dark street. *Don't look back. Keep goin', do as Ma says. She'll be fine. What the hell is she gonna do? Blast it! I need to turn this blasted wagon around and . . . no, worry about gettin' my brothers and sister to safety. To the cave. My promise to Ma. She'll catch us up as she promised. She always keeps her promises.*

Whether it's feigned confidence or he actually does believe what he is thinking, Danny snaps the reins again, encouraging the horse along.

Around the side of the Stanlow, McPharlen takes a long piss and looks at the sky as he enjoys the relief. He takes in his surrounds, smiles to himself and shivers a little at the crispness of the early morning. The sun has risen but the mountain range blocks its rays.

Then he jumps with fright. 'What the fuckin' hell, woman!'

Molly stands right in front of him. His face changes as if he has swallowed something sour. He aims the last of his piss at her feet but Molly doesn't move. She just stares at him, summoning her courage from deep within.

I need to do this. Stand here before you. To show you, to help me know that you mean nothin' to me. You may have hurt me, had your way with me, but you will not hurt or scare me or have your way with me ever again.

Because I stand before you afraid, yes, but I will not succumb or surrender to it. Damn ya to hell, ya bastard, for what ya did to me. Ya had no right! No right at all. Ya have no control, you are nothing.

Unbeknown to Molly, tears are streaming down her face. McPharlen raises his eyes to lock with hers and, with a condescending smile, lifts his hand and wipes roughly at the tears on her face, then violently grabs her jaw. 'You mountain women don't know when to walk away,' he snarls. Something passes through Molly's eyes. They glaze over and she is gone.

McPharlen's face distorts and he gasps for air, feeling a pain so extreme that he can't manage a sound. His knees give way, taking him to the ground so he is kneeling before Molly. Is he wracked with guilt and asking for her forgiveness? His hands are over his groin and now blood seeps through his trousers and fingers.

Molly has castrated him.

She turns her face to the early-morning sky. It begins to snow.

McPharlen finally topples over, still holding himself, his body draining of blood. The snowflakes hitting the ground quickly turn pink.

A few flakes hit Molly's face and bring her out of her stupor. She gasps for breath, coughing and spluttering, then looks around her and sees what she has done. She is deeply and immediately remorseful. She holds back her cries, covering her mouth with her bloody, trembling hands. Her whole body shakes. She scrambles to leave and turns straight into Sergeant Nate Clintoff!

They look at each other, neither knowing what to do next. Nate is in shock too.

He absorbs the sorry state of Molly's beaten face and her awkward stance as she holds her broken ribs, pain racking her body again as the adrenaline of the moment leaves her. Tears well in her eyes. He can't help but feel for her. But it's the fresh spray of blood on her hands and mouth that he can't get past. And of course the man dying before him. Nate witnesses the life leaving McPharlen's eyes.

There is silence all around. Pure peace as the first of the sun's rays spread across the sky. The distant caw of a crow is heard. It's dawn. A new day.

Molly's eyes flick in the direction her children went, willing them onwards. Her eyes are pleading.

Nate is torn between his vow to uphold the law, and rightful justice for the bruised and battered Molly Johnson. He hasn't seen wounds like hers since his time at war – enough evidence and grounds for him to turn a blind eye and set her free, but he's found the trooper's horse tied up at the edge of town and must address the matter of a government-issued horse without its rider. And, whether he likes it or not, the dead man at his feet.

Molly is exhausted – there is no fight left in her. Her knees buckle and she falls to the ground, her head hanging low. Her voice meek and mild, almost inaudible, she makes a final plea: 'Please. My children.'

THIRTY

Two-and-a-half days have passed. Some of the bruises on Molly's face have blackened and the swelling is subsiding. The cuts have been attended to. She sings softly to herself, 'And still I hope that the time will come when you and I will be as one.'

She stands on a stool gazing out of a little cell window – the cell she occupies at the Everton jailhouse. She looks at the snow-covered land stretched out before her and sings, 'Black, black, black is the colour of my true love's hair . . .' Heavy snow covers the ground. *No good for the children*, she thinks. Her gaze falls on the distant snow-covered mountains and she stares at them, willing her children to survive, to make the journey to Yadaka's cave.

Nate grabs a stool from the small desk once occupied by Trooper Spencer Leslie and brings it over to her cell door. 'What's out there?'

'Life.'

Through the bars, on the floor, Nate slides a shot of warm brandy, attempting to keep her calm for what lies ahead. 'They say it's going to be a very cold winter. Unprecedented snowfall this year.'

'Really.'

'One of the old black trackers that came with the troopers from the north told me. I'm amazed at their profound knowledge of the ways of the land.' He pauses for dramatic effect. 'He also said your children's tracks are gone.'

There's a tiny glint of worry in her eyes.

Nate softens his voice. 'Where are your children, Missus Johnson?' His eyes drill into her back, hoping she can feel his sincerity. He's made a promise to Louisa that he will ensure their safety. 'I can help them. I want to help them.'

The new peacekeeper of Everton can't help but feel a little guilty.

I can't throw the guilt that niggles at me. Maybe I should have turned a blind eye to Molly's crime – clearly it was the desperate act of a woman deeply wronged. But I took an oath to uphold the law and there is already one murderer on the loose. Dammit! I haven't slept a goddamn wink, fighting myself over my decision and how everything has panned out for Molly. Not to mention the tension between Louisa and I escalating as a result.

The Crown versus Molly Johnson. An all-male jury. Miss Shirley's declaration of Molly's mixed-blood heritage. The Crown's closing statement: 'Her hatred towards the white men killed by her hand is generational. Stemmed from the knowledge learnt about her heritage and her own mother's plight, by the black man who was wanted for abhorrent murders, he indeed a callous murderer himself. He encouraged her to seek revenge.'

The hearing was biased, I know, but there was nothing I could do. The only witness to Molly's truth is Danny, and he is nowhere to be found. Poor Louisa – talk about not sleeping. Fighting for all she's worth, lobbying for legislation to help battered wives, but that's never going to go through in time to help Molly Johnson. Poor woman. Oh my God, what must she be going through? But it will help others. At least she'll die knowing that a change will come one day – and soon, if Louisa has anything to do with it.

Nate is brought out of his thoughts by her voice. Molly hasn't said much to him over the few days she's been in custody, but now she's telling him, 'My children will have all the help, all the love they will ever need.' It's her hope, anyway.

There's a dull jolt and the sound of laughter. It's not boisterous, just filled with satisfaction and jubilation. Molly cranes her neck to see, to her right, a bag of flour swinging from a gibbet, a ringed slipknot noose tight around the sack. Troopers are checking the tautness of the rope and the craftsmanship of the structure they have just erected. It's brand new and holds up pretty well. Preparations are complete for the town's first execution – the execution of Molly Johnson, a drover's wife. She's making history today. The troopers pick up their tools, idly chatting.

Molly brings her focus back to the mountains in the distance, the snow-dusted snow gums that border the boundary of cleared land for the expansion to Everton, and begins to hum softly.

The front door to the jailhouse bursts open and in bustles Louisa Clintoff, flustered. She is holding a tray of hot food and a pair of blood-red shoes, and has a musk-pink dress draped over one arm. The shoes are the ones she wore to the ball in Melbourne held in her and Nate's honour.

Nate moves to greet her but she steps back, a frostiness still between them. She is more concerned with Missus Johnson than with showing affection to her husband. In a hushed but stern tone she says, 'Sorry, Nate. Sorry to intrude.'

'Louisa, this is no place for a woman.' Nate wishes he could take back his words as soon as they leave his mouth.

'Really? Well, there's a woman in there, behind bars and awaiting execution,' Louisa retorts. 'There must be something we can do to get a stay of execution. Has a doctor examined her? Her mind? She's just given birth and lost a child, and fears for her others. Nate?'

'Louisa, please. The evidence against her is mountainous. I witnessed the murder of one man, the knife in her hand before me. His blood splattered on her face.'

'So you saw her battered face under his blood – that could be considered an act of provocation. Nate, we heard the boy's assumption about your injury. That mindset is indicative of what they live with. Missus Johnson has experienced cumulative abuse at the hands of her husband.'

'We have no witnesses.'

'There rarely are.'

They stare each other down, both determined to hold their position on this. Nate reluctantly says, 'And she's confessed.'

This hits Louisa hard, like a punch to the stomach.

Nate can only offer a lame smile. He loves his wife dearly and admires her caring and determined spirit, her intelligent mind and sharp wit.

Knowing she is defeated for now, she offers, 'Is she allowed a nice meal and a change of clothes?'

Holding out his hands, Nate says, 'Thank you, I'll see that she gets it.' But Louisa manoeuvres past him and makes her way over to the cell.

As she approaches, her bravado disappears with each step. 'Hello?' she says.

Molly continues humming and looking out the cell window.

Louisa is a little lost as to what to say next. 'Please, I'm here as a . . . to . . .'

There's a long silence. Molly doesn't move or say anything. Louisa's idea seems foolish now, and she turns to go.

'Ya put up a good argument there.'

Quickly turning back to Molly, Louisa takes this opportunity to reach out to her. 'Telling the sergeant . . . or me, where your children are would be far better. Danny would be such a great help to you and your case.'

Molly turns to face Louisa. 'And if he's not?'

Louisa can't answer.

'They see me die. They're dragged through this for what? And then what happens? Where will they go? Who'll watch over them?'

Molly pauses, letting her words hang in the air. She knows Nate is listening. She hopes to make them understand her reasons for not talking. 'No. I die knowin' they're safe . . . and protected and loved . . . by family.'

Hesitantly, Louisa adds, 'You can't be sure of that, either.'

With no hesitation at all Molly comes back with 'Danny is a good boy. Smart. Strong . . .'

An awkward moment passes between them. Molly turns back to the cell window. Is there a hint of doubt there? Has Louisa hit a nerve here with Molly?

Louisa understands now that this woman is prepared to die for her children's future.

'Ya husband sent for ya?' asks Molly suddenly.

'No, I thought you could do with a good meal and a change of clothes.'

'What else do ya think I need?' Molly turns to face Louisa, stern.

She holds her own despite her predicament. Louisa places the dress, shoes and tray of food on the nearby stool.

'I didn't mean to intrude.'

Molly turns away. Then Louisa spies, on the stretcher-bed, a copy of her women's journal, *The Dawn*. It's a double-sided single page, her first publication. The headline screams *Battered wives: is it purely a husband's right?* She looks at Nate, knowing he must have given it to Molly – perhaps in the hope she would read it and open up to him. Something unspoken passes between Nate and Louisa as he offers her a small, heartfelt smile and a slight shrug of his shoulders. He tried, hoping to get Molly to trust him.

Louisa turns back to Molly, still gazing through the cell window, 'Ah, my journal. And the audacity of Nate. I guess he thought it might help you to know that we care.' Molly looks back at her, seeing Louisa pointing to the stretcher-bed where the page lies, then back to the world outside her cell. It begins to snow again and they can hear the soft sound of it falling on the wooden-slat roof of the jailhouse. Molly closes her eyes to listen. It's one of the final sounds she'll hear, and it's soothing.

'You write from the outside,' she says.

Louisa is taken aback. She prides herself on her ability as a writer to get inside her subject's mind. And considering her own sister died at the hands of her husband, a so-called gentleman, she says, 'I was trying to give voice to an issue that has been kept silent for far too long.' Molly doesn't say anything so Louisa continues, unable to disguise her frustration. 'Trying to give women a voice.'

Molly turns to her. 'I could only hear – *you*.'

An uneasy silence falls between the two women as Louisa considers what Molly has said. It's Louisa who breaks it, saying, 'Point made. Thank you.' She smooths her dress, slightly embarrassed by the comment. *Dammit, the woman is right.*

Molly turns again to look towards the mountains in the distance, still willing her children to make it. *Perhaps they're in the warmth of the cave by now?* She fills her mind with an image of her children happy, safe and warm around a camp fire, with someone fussing over their needs.

Louisa grabs Nate's chair from behind his desk, giving him a look that says, 'Please leave.' He does.

She places the chair before the bars and sits down, notepad and pencil in hand. After a few moments, Molly turns to look at her. *Can I really trust you?*

You can trust me.

Louisa takes the lead. 'Can I hear you? Your story, Missus Johnson?'

'Molly ... my name is Molly.'

'Can I hear your story, Molly?'

Taking a deep breath, and for the first time in a long time, Molly smiles. A smile weighted with much sorrow. 'For my children. Let not my sin overshadow my children knowin' my love for them.'

THIRTY-ONE

Bare, cold, snow-covered feet step up to the gibbet hesitantly, as if weighted with lead. Molly told Louisa she wouldn't wear the shoes. It wouldn't be her, and she wants to honour her mother. But mostly she wants to feel ... alive, her senses tingling from her head to her toes, as she takes her last steps and last breaths. *Feel that sharp cold, that sting in the air ...*

Molly looks at the rope and falters. Nate grabs her elbow, steadying her. One more step to go and she will have reached the top of the gibbet platform. She begins to search the crowd, looking for someone.

The large trooper who stands before her takes the slipknot and holds it out to Molly. Nate directs her to it. He turns away as the trooper places it around her neck and pulls on it, tightening it. Molly is jolted back to reality, to where she is standing and what is about to happen. She looks down to see the rope resting on her chest, rising and falling with each shallow, nervous breath.

Nate steps away and stands to the side. He can't look at her, and appears very distressed himself.

I wish I'd let her go to be with her children, let the law of the mountain rule for the very last time, an eye for an eye.

But how could I? There was no mistaking all the evidence I found against her, especially in the murder of Trooper Leslie. For my own sanity I have to believe I did the right thing. The murder of her husband could be self-defence, maybe. Her son would have made a perfect witness, having seen what he saw time and time again. But an innocent trooper trying to do his duty? That's what pushed Molly's conviction to the death penalty.

Nate shakes his head to clear his thoughts.

Molly stands on the gibbet, hands tied behind her back, rope around her neck. Judge Eisenmangher stands beside her and unrolls a scroll to read out the charges laid against her: 'You, Molly Johnson, shall be hanged by the neck until dead.'

Molly searches the crowd. A sea of stern male faces stare back at her.

Judge Eisenmangher continues: 'For the murders of John McPharlen, Trooper Spencer Leslie and your husband, Joe Johnson.'

Molly spots Louisa Clintoff pushing her way through the crowd, her black cape held tight around her. They lock eyes. Two other women, one of them Elpida Sava, come to Louisa's side. They hold blankets drapped over their dresses, and all three are wearing their brightest item of clothing: a pair of shoes, gloves and a scarf. They appear to be a little on edge. It's eerily quiet.

Judge Eisenmangher leaves the platform, passing Nate, who is looking down at his wife, distressed.

Molly and Louisa exchange subtle nods, a silent pact made

between them. Molly's gaze finds the solace of the snow-covered mountains. It's a stunning sight, picture perfect.

Louisa and the two women by her side remove their capes to reveal aprons over their dresses. There is script written in charcoal on them: *'Hear her! Battered wives are powerless! Legislate women's rights now!'* The women join hands and step forward. Some of the men notice, grunting their disapproval.

Nate is deeply moved by his wife's protest, proud of her bravery. But he cannot waver from his appointed position of law of Everton. He too looks to the mountains for comfort and strength. The large trooper steps up behind Molly. Nate struggles to give the final nod. One of the women starts to cry.

Molly begins to mumble her da's favourite song: 'And still I hope that the time will come when you and I will be as one.' The snow on her feet starts to send a tingling sensation through her body, travelling fast up her legs, her subconscious taking over.

And now, there before me is the smilin' face of Delphi. The sweet girl holds up a daisy-chain necklace – not a hangman's slipknot, but precious little daisy flowers neatly twisted and entwined to form the perfect necklace.

Oh look, there are Joe Junior and Henry James laughin' and throwin' snow at each other. See them wave to me? I hope they behave. My little rascals.

And now out from behind a snow gum it's my Danny-boy. There he is. My beautiful, carin' boy – no, my young man – a man long before his time with all he has witnessed in his twelve short years. See, he smiles and nods to me, encouragin' me to go. See, he holds up his fist and blows through it, just as I showed him. His fingers spring open to send this breath and words on the wings of the crow that flies overhead and carries them to me. *Always with you* . . .

I feel my heart tear. My insides drop and I feel the warmth of my own piss runnin' down my legs. But I will not fall. I will not drop. I am a woman. A Ngarigo woman – so much more than a drover's wife.

My Danny turns to go. He steps out, lively with determination, and I know he and the others are fine. But wait – he turns to give me one final look, and I know I will be remembered.

My children give me strength and focus. *The mountains – look to the mountains. That's home . . .*

Nate clears his throat, still afraid to look at Molly, whose eyes are glazed with tears. *Good God, I really have to do this. None of this was in the brief. Come to Australia and run a sleepy town in the high country.*

He can't stand it any longer. *Prolonging this isn't going to help anyone.* He turns to the trooper and nods sharply, then immediately brings his focus back to his wife. She will not turn away and covers her mouth with her gloved hands, silencing her screams as the trooper steps forward.

The crow calls to me as it circles again above. Encouragin' me to lift my spirit, to give my soul. And I do and I'm gone on its wings . . .

High up in the snow-covered mountains, a tree branch cracks and snaps under the weight of the snow. Molly's boys spin around in fright and Henry James, worn out, falls over in the deep snow. Exhausted, Danny carries a frostbitten Delphi on his back. Tiny icicles are forming on her closed lashes. It's hard to tell whether the little one is dead or sleeping.

The children are dwarfed by the landscape around them. With snow up to their knees, Joe Junior helps his little brother up and they trudge on. They are close to giving up, exhausted and frighteningly cold.

Danny surveys the landscape desperately. They have reached the area that looks as if someone has cleared a space, making a perfect circle. His eyes flick frantically from boulder to boulder, looking for the three large 'emu eggs'. He is on the verge of tears, the burden of saving them all weighing upon him. He looks to the left. He looks to the right. There are plenty of boulders, but no three in a row in the perfect shape of large emu eggs.

Then, from the corner of his eye, in the distance he sees a woman, her fire-red hair catching his attention. She stands at the side of a boulder. Danny blinks and she is gone. Thinking he might be seeing things, he comes further around to see where she went and sees the three large boulders standing before him, bold and strong. He's made it! He's done it, as he said he would, for his ma.

His brothers come to stand beside him and he nods his head towards the boulders, saying, 'It's there. The cave, just beyond the three boulders that look like giant emu eggs.'

True to their young innocent minds, Joe Junior and Henry James tilt their heads, trying to see the 'emu egg' aspect. They screw up their noses. 'Maybe wombat droppings,' Joe Junior whispers with a cheeky grin to his little brother, who agrees. Danny smiles at his brothers. As dire as the conditions are, *these two rascals ...*

He adds, 'Food, shelter and, in the spring, people.'

Feeling confident, the brothers take each other's hands and trudge through the snow, following the path of the fair-skinned Aboriginal woman with the fiery red hair. Together they disappear behind the boulders.

EPILOGUE

'When we came back down from the mountains, I was sixteen. I heard many a story about my ma's so-called man-hating rampage. ' "A mad woman filled with hate," and "It's the black in her", people were sayin'. But then there was the story from Louisa Clintoff.'

Danny's voice is deep, manly, gentle and wise for his thirty-two years. He has grown into a handsome, intelligent young man, tall and strong. He stands beside his new fireplace. A framed old newspaper article with the masthead *The Dawn* in large black print sits on the mantel. In smaller print, the headline reads: *The Drover's Wife: Molly Johnson's Story.*

'In her writing Louisa asks, "A crime or justice?" Survival, I say. Survival, as I, her eldest son, knows it to have been.'

Danny moves over to sit on the couch with his beautiful, pregnant, dark-skinned Aboriginal wife, Nell. She's twenty-eight years old. Danny takes her hand and kisses it gently. Before them, sitting on a possum-skin rug, are their six children, ranging in age from two to twelve and varying in skin colour from brown to olive to fair with red hair and freckles, just like their great-grandmother, Black Mary – or Waraganj, as they prefer to call her. They all listen attentively to their father.

'It's the story I lived, it's the story I have told and will retell. The story of survival I'll pass down.'

Each evening before bed, for all their entertainment, there is a story, which always leads to a re-enactment. Sometimes it's their father reading to them or telling this very story, or their mother telling Dreaming stories of the land and how it came to be. Other times, the children re-enact a story they love and know well – the Bullock Story, paying homage to the legend of their grandma Molly Johnson. Tonight, the children will play-act that very story, the beloved Bullock Story, the story that Danny lived and has now passed on to his children.

He loves retelling this story – how Yadaka, a great man, father and warrior, acted out the bullock. He smiles at the memory but then sadness fills his eyes for a fleeting moment that only his wife sees – and only she knows what it means.

The children jump to their feet to tell what's become their story of how their grandma brought a big wild grey bullock down with a single shot, right between the eyes. Three of the younger children act out being caught in front of the bullock like their Uncle Joe, who is now a drover like their Grandfather Joe was. Their Uncle Henry James is a businessman who lives in Melbourne, married to a 'lady' who doesn't like to visit much, but he always makes sure she comes with him and the children for a special day the brothers share. Their Aunty Delphi is overseas, living in Paris. She hasn't been back home since she left at the age of sixteen.

Soon, though, everyone will be home for the twelfth birthday of Mirribi, Danny and Nell's eldest son. Mirribi will also go through the final stage of his men's-business ceremony – the one his father and uncles learnt in the high country with their Ngarigo family. Their Uncle Bulbarai passed the ceremony on to them in some haste – he knew time was running out for ancient practices. Modern ways were invading and destroying everything the Ngarigo held dear and believed in for their survival. It was after Joe Junior's and Henry

James's initiation that Molly's children came back down from the mountains.

Danny and his brothers are grateful and honoured to be able to carry on something from a culture so ancient, from their family, their Aboriginal family. They hold the knowledge with great pride, Danny more so than the others, but nonetheless they all stand their ground in defending their culture and countrymen when needed.

In the Story of the Bullock Mirribi acts as a young Danny, drawing in the dirt floor; Danny's eldest daughter, Molly-Mary, acts out his ma. He can see his mother in his daughter, not so much in looks but in temperament.

Danny and Nell have renovated Molly's old shanty to a humble homestead, where the old snow gum still stands sentinel out front. Next to the tree now, though, is a horse rail, and often Danny hears riders say they've seen an Aboriginal man standing there, looking over the place. 'But when ya get closer, he's gone.'

Danny just smiles, and replies, 'Yep, that sounds about right.'

He ploughed and packed that old track that was barely visible, making the property accessible. Nothing to hide here. But there is a significant-sized fence and gate that you go through to get to the back door, and you have to pass two vicious-looking dogs called Alli and Gator.

And every evening, Danny still sweeps the top layer of dirt to rid it of the day's foot traffic, 'so I know who is about, be it animal or man'.

His eldest daughter, her voice deep and husky like her grandma's, says, 'Gun. Now. Slow.' Mirribi hands her a make-believe gun, but then their father rips off his shirt to display tribal markings on his chest, a badge of honour from his people. He stomps at the floorboards with his bare feet and begins to mimic the bullock, just as Yadaka did all those years ago.

This Story of the Bullock is also a journey from where the Johnsons have come. Danny told it to the Ngarigo, and they in turn added it to the principles and practice of their ancient culture of mimicry and dance, building it up with song and movement.

Danny and his siblings loved that the story was honoured by the Ngarigo for their ma's bravery and respect for her plight, and that it brought her into the family clan. It was a way they could all remember Molly, but also a way the clan could share in her. It was a proud moment for Danny when the men, women and children dressed and painted up to perform the story for them.

Tonight, though, there is no paint or singing or ancient musical instruments – just a simplified version that Danny's children have created.

Molly-Mary brings the pretend shotgun up to shoot the bullock. They are all very good in their play-acting – they have done this before. It's a much-loved story that has been told many times over.

Mirribi whispers to his sister, 'Shoot 'im!'

She shouts, 'Bang!' and makes the pretend shotgun recoil in her arms as their father, play-acting the bullock, falls to the ground, dead. The children applaud and throw themselves on him. His wife claps and laughs, praising them in her mother tongue of the Yirrkala. She looks lovingly at them all as Danny engulfs his children in his big arms.

Their laughter and squeals of delight can be heard from outside. Molly's old shanty is now a large family home with a verandah wrapping all the way around it. It sits in the light of the fire pit that still burns and, now, electric lights that highlight every room through the glass windows. Smoke rises from the old river-rock chimney at one end and from a new chimney that warms the shanty's new extension. It's picture perfect, this property and homestead sitting in the still of the beautiful autumn night. The large, dark form of the mountain range still stands like a fortress wall before them, but the thick scrub that once surrounded the shanty is gone.

From inside, Molly-Mary asks her father to tell them a poem. They all gather to sit with him on the possum rug. The baby sits on her father's lap and snuggles into his chest, sucking her thumb. He begins: 'Monaro. Ngarigo. Walgalu. Country. Water. Life force. Runs through our veins. Boundaries. Songlines, we sit down this side. Family. Mother. Deep ancient connection ...'

Outside, a blanket of brilliant stars fills the sky and a new moon smiles down on the landscape below.

By the old snow gum a woman stands. They have a visitor. Oh, no – wait ... It's the feminine shape of the tree trunk, exaggerated by the dark night and the firelight. Or is it?

Oh, to see these trees after an autumn shower ... it's this rare beauty that reminds me why I stay ...

Molly Johnson's legend and family live on.

On Country.

AUTHOR'S NOTE

What a joy and awesome learning experience it was to write this novel. In Aboriginal words, it was Deadly(!) – hard work, but I loved it. I love history. My love for history came about when I was a teenager. I was fourteen, and wanted to understand more about my Aboriginality – what my mother and grandparents had lost due to government policy not allowing them to pass on our culture. I was determined to fill in the gaps in our history. Through this research, and listening to oral stories from my elders, I put the pieces of our historical past together and found my spiritual self. My culture has become my solid foundation, and has held me in good stead ever since.

As a writer I love drawing from my own family history, and Australian history in general, to inspire the settings, situations and contexts for my fictional characters, bringing a story to life through imagination. This is how I came to create the fictitious world of Molly Johnson.

I have carried this story with me for forty-two years. My mother would read 'The Drover's Wife' by Henry Lawson to me as a little girl. I would always stop her and recite the famous last line – 'Ma, I won't never go a drovin'.' Then, in 2006 I was in the Australian Snowy Mountains shooting a film called *Jindabyne* with director Ray Lawrence, and I made a pact with my ancestors, and those of the land I was standing on, and set a goal for myself that I would be back on that beautiful country of the Ngarigo/Walgalu to make and star in a film of *The Drover's Wife*. As fate would have it, as I was doing the final proofread on this novel getting it ready for publication I was also starting pre-production on my first feature film, *The Drover's Wife the Legend of Molly Johnson*. How's that for the ancestors answering my prayers?

But this all began with a play I wrote for Belvoir St Theatre, with the wonderful support of the Balnaves Foundation and the Balnaves Fellowship in 2014, which allowed me to pen the script. It went on to open in late 2016 to a limited sold-out season of thirty-three shows. The production cleaned up, winning a dozen or more awards in 2017. On the back of the play's success I secured a book deal with Penguin Random House, and the go-ahead for a feature film.

I am proud and happy to say that there is a difference to the three genres that this story encompasses: theatre, film, novel. The novel follows a similar structure to the film, and picks up on the backstories of the characters, which allowed me to explore greater depth and development of story. The novel of course allows the reader to get inside the characters' heads, to read their inner thoughts. I found that a little difficult to convey at first, and was reminded of one of my first ever writer notes for TV: the mentor writer/script editor said, 'If you ever hand a script in again with the character talking to itself, you'll be shot!' So, it took a while to allow myself to write the characters' inner thoughts into the novel. LOL!

I would like to thank my elders for their support and guidance: Aunty Honor Cleary, Uncle Michael Mace, Aunty Lynelle 'Minnie' Mace, Ma Mace (RIP) and Francis Adkins (family in-law and researcher of 'The Test of Endurance' for Hazel Mace, which was used to inform Yadaka's story). Uncle Hans Pearson and Sean Choolburra of the Guu Gu Yimithirr; Paul House of the Ngambri Walgalu; and Aunty Iris Smith, Aunty Doris Paton and elder Aunty Rachel

Mullett of the Monaro Ngarigo for the permission to use the Ngarigo language.

The story I have created of the Ngarigo/Walgalu is based on general fact, but fictionalised to protect traditional and cultural practice.

Writing *The Drover's Wife* in all its forms could not have been possible without the unwavering love, belief and support from my partner in life and business Bain, who works tirelessly to get my ideas up.

I failed English at school. So, to have written a play, a film and now this novel – which I am so proud of – makes me feel pretty good about myself! And I hope I give inspiration to others.

Thanks to all the people who helped us to make all of these projects come to fruition, and to all who worked hard to get this book out.

A special mention and a big Thank You to Bain, Manda, Raf, Lysander and my dog, Odi.

Lastly, thank you for the inspiration, Henry Lawson. I reckon he and my mum would be toasting each other in the afterlife just about now. Cheers, Ma!

Peace, love and light,

Leah x
Altjeringa yirra Baiame!

PS. I hope to do another.